Paul Levy

Exam Practice
Workbook

Edexcel
GCSE Physics

Contents

Unit P1: Universal Physics

Unit P2: Physics for Your Future

Unit P3: Application of Physics

Answers (found at the centre of the book)

Periodic Table (found on the inside back cover)

Questions labelled with an asterisk (*) are ones where the quality of your written communication will be assessed – you should take particular care with your spelling, punctuation and grammar, as well as the clarity of expression, on these questions.

1. State the name of the model of the Solar System in which the Earth was thought to be at the centre. (1)

2. To test if this model was right, Galileo made observations of Venus and another planet. What is the name of the other planet? (1)

3. The geocentric model states that everything orbits the Earth. What did Galileo see when he looked at Jupiter that convinced him that this model is **not** correct? (2)

4. We now accept that the Sun is at the centre of our Solar System. What name is given to this model? (1)

5. Give **two** reasons why the geocentric model of the Universe was accepted for so many years.

   (a) (1)

   (b) (1)

6. **(a)** Why was it more difficult to discover the planet Neptune than Uranus? (1)

   (b) How was Neptune discovered? (2)

7. Label the diagram of a wave below to show wavelength and amplitude. (2)

8. What is meant by the **frequency** of a wave? (2)

9. Ellie is generating a wave by moving one end of a rope that is fixed to a wall. She moves it up and down two times every second.

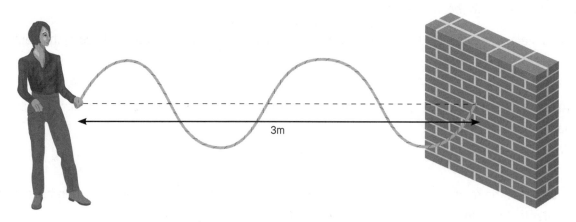

In the diagram, Ellie is 3m away from the wall.

(a) What is the frequency of the wave generated? Give your answer in hertz (Hz), that is, the number of waves per second. (1)

....

(b) What is the wavelength of the wave generated? (1)

....

(c) What type of wave is this? (1)

....

10. The diagram below shows a wave travelling along a 'slinky' spring. The hand is moving backwards and forwards, three times a second.

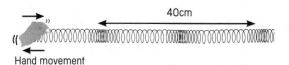

Hand movement

(a) What is the frequency of the wave generated? Give your answer in hertz (Hz). (1)

....

(b) What is its wavelength? (1)

....

(c) What is the name of this type of wave? (1)

....

11. State **two** differences and **one** similarity between transverse waves and longitudinal waves.

Differences:

(a) .... (1)

(b) .... (1)

Similarity:

(c) .... (1)

12. A sound wave has a frequency of 200Hz. Its wavelength is 1.70m. Calculate the speed of the wave. (2)

....

....

13. A water wave is seen to move a distance of 3m in a time of 12 seconds. Calculate the speed of the wave. (1)

....

14. (a) A light wave travels from glass to air. What happens to the direction of the wave as it passes into the air? (1)

....

(b) Not all of the light passes into the air. What happens to the rest of it? (1)

....

15. Visible light can be used to observe the Universe. Name the **three** ways that such observations can be made.

(a) .... (1)

(b) .... (1)

(c) .... (1)

16. On the diagram of a converging lens, below, label the **focus** and **focal length**. (2)

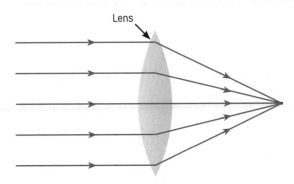

Lens

17. Given a converging lens and a piece of paper to act as a screen, explain how to find the focal length of the lens. (4)

_____

_____

_____

_____

_____

18. Give the names of the **two** converging lenses that are used to make a simple telescope.

(a) _____ (1)

(b) _____ (1)

19. The diagram of a reflecting telescope is shown below.

A Reflecting Telescope

Eyepiece (convex) lens

Parabolic mirror

Flat mirror

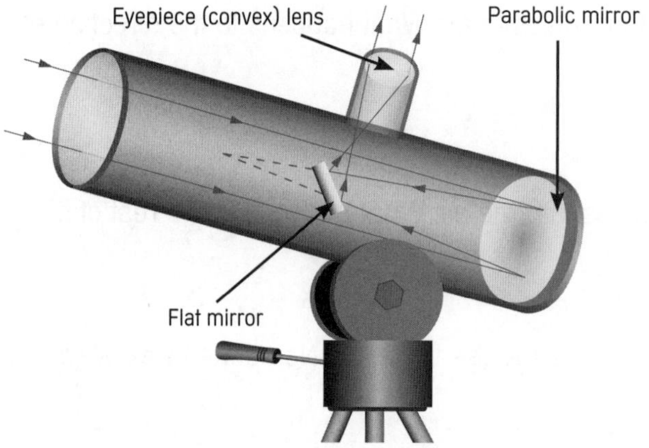

Explain how a reflecting telescope works. (3)

_____

_____

_____

_____

_____

_____

20. The Universe can be observed by means of visible light with the naked eye, photography and the telescope. Complete the following table to show **one** advantage and **one** disadvantage of each method. (3)

	Advantage	Disadvantage
Naked eye		
Photography		
Telescope		

21. Describe the purpose of the objective and the eyepiece lens in a simple refracting telescope.

(a) Objective .... (1)

(b) Eyepiece .... (1)

*22. Describe how a simple telescope works and compare it to a reflecting telescope. (6)

....

....

....

....

....

....

....

....

....

....

....

....

(Total: .... **/ 53)**

23.

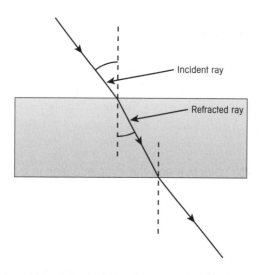

Incident ray

Refracted ray

Complete the diagram above, of a ray of light passing from air into a glass block, to show:

(a) the normal (1)

(b) the angle of incidence (1)

(c) the angle of refraction. (1)

24. What happens to the speed of the light as it moves into the glass? (1)

25. **(a)** A radio station broadcasts on a wavelength of 252m. If the speed of the waves is $3 \times 10^8 \text{ms}^{-1}$, calculate the frequency of the waves. Show your working. (2)

(b) 'The Bay' radio station transmits on a frequency of 96.9MHz ($1\text{MHz} = 10^6\text{Hz}$). Calculate its wavelength. Show your working. (2)

(Total: .... / 8)

Questions labelled with an asterisk (*) are ones where the quality of your written communication will be assessed – you should take particular care with your spelling, punctuation and grammar, as well as the clarity of expression, on these questions.

1. What type of electromagnetic radiation is used to take pictures of the inside of a person's body? (1)

A ☐ Microwaves   B ☐ Ultraviolet

C ☐ X-rays   D ☐ Visible light

2. Complete the diagram below to show what happens to white light when it hits a glass prism. (4)

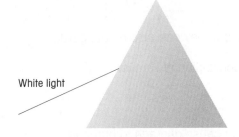

White light

3. Visible light is one part of the family of electromagnetic waves, called the electromagnetic spectrum. The other members are **X-rays**, **ultraviolet**, **radio waves**, **infrared**, **microwaves** and **gamma rays**. Arrange these in the correct order in the table below. (2)

Highest Frequency   Lowest Frequency

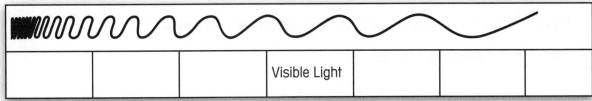

			Visible Light			

4. Write **true** or **false** alongside each of these statements about electromagnetic waves.

(a) Electromagnetic waves are longitudinal waves. _____ (1)

(b) Different types of electromagnetic wave carry energy. _____ (1)

(c) Sound is part of the electromagnetic spectrum. _____ (1)

(d) Electromagnetic waves travel at different speeds. _____ (1)

5. Which type of electromagnetic radiation is used:

(a) to send information to and from satellites? _____ (1)

(b) in sunbeds (to give a sun tan)? _____ (1)

(c) in remote controls for TVs and DVD players? _____ (1)

(d) with fluorescent lamps to security-code electrical goods? _____ (1)

6. What harmful effects does excessive exposure to ultraviolet radiation have? (2)

....

....

....

7. The higher the frequency of the waves in the electromagnetic spectrum, the more damage they can do. Name the part of the spectrum that is, therefore, most dangerous. (1)

....

8. **(a)** X-rays can be very useful but they can also be dangerous.

    (i) Describe **one** useful application of X-rays. (1)

....

    (ii) Explain why X-rays can cause damage to humans. (1)

....

    (b) Why do microwaves and X-rays have different properties? (1)

....

9. Police helicopters are often equipped with thermal imaging equipment. (4)

Explain how this helps the police.

....

....

....

....

....

....

....

10. Johann Ritter discovered ultraviolet waves in 1801. Who was the scientist that discovered infrared waves in the year 1800? (1)

....

11. Explain how radiographers use X-rays to produce images of a patient's bones to diagnose a fracture in the arm bone. (4)

....

....

....

....

....

12. Microwaves and infrared waves are both used for cooking. Microwaves can penetrate food to a depth of 3-4cm. Infrared rays are absorbed by the surface of the food.

(a) Explain why microwave ovens can be used to defrost food even though they carry less energy than infrared waves into the food. (2)

....

....

....

(b) Why are infrared waves not suitable to defrost most foods? (2)

....

....

....

13. **(a)** Alpha, beta and gamma radiation are ionising radiations. What does this mean? (2)

....

....

....

(b) Gamma rays can be used to kill cancer cells. They are also dangerous. Explain why. (2)

....

....

....

14. **(a)** What type of electromagnetic radiation is used to transmit signals between mobile phones and phone masts? (1)

....

(b) What are the dangers associated with excessive exposure to this type of radiation? (2)

....

....

....

15. The following extract is from a newspaper article.

> New findings suggest that you could be frying your brain with every mobile call you make. Scientists have proved that mobile phones can cause a significant increase in the temperature of cells in localised parts of the brain.

(a) Based on what you know about electromagnetic radiation used by mobile phones, do you think this could be possible? Explain your answer. (2)

(b) What the article does not tell you is that mobile phones can raise the temperature of the brain by about 0.1 °C, but the brain's natural temperature fluctuations can be greater than this.

Taking into account this extra information, do you think that the rise in brain temperature caused by mobile phones could be dangerous? Explain your answer. (2)

16. Explain *either* how William Herschel discovered infrared waves *or* how Johann Ritter discovered ultraviolet waves. (2)

(Total: ...... / 47)

Questions labelled with an asterisk (*) are ones where the quality of your written communication will be assessed – you should take particular care with your spelling, punctuation and grammar, as well as the clarity of expression, on these questions.

1. The diagram below shows our Solar System.

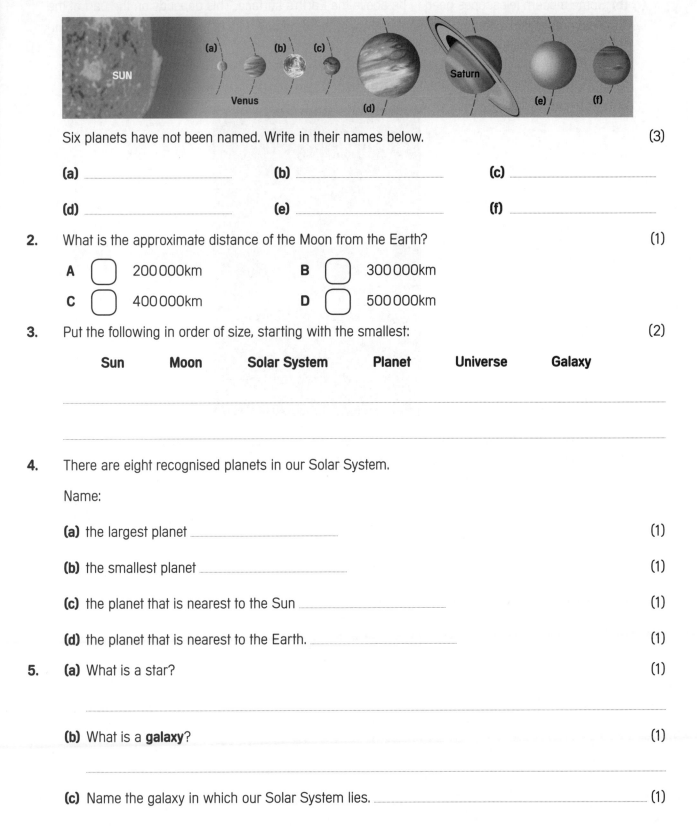

Six planets have not been named. Write in their names below. (3)

(a) .... **(b)** .... **(c)** ....

(d) .... **(e)** .... **(f)** ....

2. What is the approximate distance of the Moon from the Earth? (1)

A ☐ 200 000km   B ☐ 300 000km

C ☐ 400 000km   D ☐ 500 000km

3. Put the following in order of size, starting with the smallest: (2)

Sun   Moon   Solar System   Planet   Universe   Galaxy

....

....

4. There are eight recognised planets in our Solar System.

Name:

(a) the largest planet .... (1)

(b) the smallest planet .... (1)

(c) the planet that is nearest to the Sun .... (1)

(d) the planet that is nearest to the Earth. .... (1)

5. (a) What is a star? (1)

....

(b) What is a **galaxy**? (1)

....

(c) Name the galaxy in which our Solar System lies. .... (1)

P1 Waves and the Universe

6. (a) Apart from visible light, name **one** other part of the electromagnetic spectrum that modern telescopes use. (1)

(b) Some modern telescopes need to be above the Earth's surface. This depends on the part of the electromagnetic spectrum in which they operate. Name **one** type of telescope that will only work above the surface of the Earth. (1)

7.

The Hubble Space Telescope was developed to enable high-magnification images to be made of the Universe. Describe **one** thing that it has discovered. (2)

8. A radio telescope at Cambridge University discovered a strange pulsing radio signal in 1968. How have astronomers explained this? (4)

9. The Planck Observatory satellite has collected an enormous amount of data. What has this allowed astronomers to measure? (2)

....

....

10. There are basically **two** ways to look for intelligent life in the Universe.
What are they?

(a) .... (1)

(b) .... (1)

11. Unmanned space crafts are often used in space exploration. Give **two** reasons why.

(a) .... (1)

(b) .... (1)

12. In 1992, NASA set up **SETI**. What is SETI? (2)

....

....

13. There are different stages in the life cycle of a star of about the same mass as our Sun:
white dwarf, main sequence star, nebula, red giant. Write these below in their correct order. (2)

....

....

14. Explain what is meant by a **main sequence star**. (3)

....

....

....

....

....

....

15. There are two theories of how the Universe began: the **Steady State** and the **Big Bang**. Outline each of these theories.

(a) Steady State (2)

....

....

....

(b) Big Bang (3)

....

....

....

(c) Name the **two** pieces of evidence that support the Big Bang Theory. (2)

....

....

16. The Sun and Moon appear to be about the same size in the sky, but the Moon is very much smaller than the Sun. How do you account for this? (2)

....

....

....

(Total: .... / 43)

Higher Tier

17. Read the following information about electromagnetic radiation.

> Nearly 99% of the UV radiation that strikes our atmosphere is absorbed by the ozone layer. In addition, short-wavelength UV radiation is scattered much more by the atmosphere than radiation with longer wavelengths.

Use this information to explain why telescopes that detect UV radiation from outer space do not work if they are ground-based. (2)

....

....

....

....

continued...

18. The two flow diagrams below show the cycle of change that occurs when a star dies. Each circle represents a different stage in the cycle.

(a) Complete each circle in the cycle, using the following words: (5)

supernova **red giant** **neutron star** **red supergiant** **white dwarf**

(b) Explain what effect gravity has at **Stage A**. (2)

....

....

....

(c) Explain what happens during **Stage B**. (3)

....

....

....

....

....

....

....

....

continued...

19. **(a)** What evidence is there that the Universe is expanding? Explain your answer. (4)

(b) The Steady State Theory also says that the Universe is expanding. Why don't we accept this theory? (3)

20. The diagram below shows a spectrum from the Sun and two other stars in distant galaxies. Each of the lines represents a particular wavelength of electromagnetic radiation.

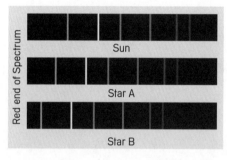

(a) What does the spectrum of Star A tell us about its movement? (1)

(b) (i) What does the spectrum of Star B tell us about its movement in relation to Star A? (2)

(ii) What can you deduce from this about its distance from us compared to Star A? (1)

(c) What does this tell us about the expansion of the Universe? (2)

(Total: .... / 25)

Questions labelled with an asterisk (*) are ones where the quality of your written communication will be assessed – you should take particular care with your spelling, punctuation and grammar, as well as the clarity of expression, on these questions.

1. Complete the information below about waves, using the following words: (5)

    infrasound   **audible range**   **longitudinal**   **ultrasound**   **vibrates**

    Sound is produced when something .... and travels as a
    .... wave.

    If a sound is within the ...., it can be heard.

    If the frequency of the sound is above 20 000Hz, it is known as ....

    If the frequency of the sound is below 20Hz, it is known as ....

2. Name **two** uses of ultrasound. (2)

3. Many animals communicate using infrasound. Give **one** example of such an animal. (1)

4. State the name of the wave caused by earthquakes or explosions. (1)

5. **Two** types of these waves are emitted. What are they called? (2)

6. Infrasound waves are emitted by meteors and meteorites that enter the Earth's atmosphere.
    Name **one** other natural source of infrasound (other than animals). (1)

7. What is a **tsunami** and how is it caused? (1)

8. Why is it difficult for scientists to predict when a tsunami will occur? (2)

9. The diagram below shows one use of ultrasound.

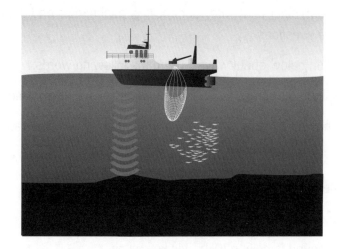

(a) Using the diagram to help you, outline how ultrasound can be used to find the depth of the seabed. (3)

....

....

....

(b) The time taken for the reflected signal to arrive back at the ship is 2s. If the velocity of the ultrasound is 1500m/s in the water, calculate the depth of the seabed. (Depth = Speed × $\frac{1}{2}$ Time) (2)

....

....

*10. The Earth's surface is split into large **plates**. Describe how these plates can cause earthquakes. (6)

....

....

....

....

....

....

....

....

11. The diagram below shows a **seismometer**. This is an instrument used to detect the vibrations from earthquakes.

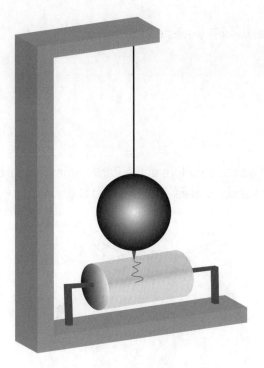

(a) Outline how a seismometer works. (3)

....

....

....

(b) How can data from seismometers enable the location of an earthquake to be found? (2)

....

....

....

(Total: .... / 31)

12. Give **two** differences between P waves and S waves. (2)

....

....

....

13. The diagram below shows the structure of the Earth. An earthquake occurs at point A.
It produces two types of shock waves: P waves and S waves.

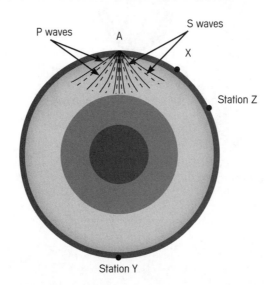

(a) Complete the diagram to show the paths of the P waves and S waves through the Earth. (3)

(b) State, with reasons, whether P waves, S waves or both will reach:

   (i) Station Z (2)

....

....

   (ii) Station Y (2)

....

....

(Total: .... **/ 9)**

Questions labelled with an asterisk (*) are ones where the quality of your written communication will be assessed – you should take particular care with your spelling, punctuation and grammar, as well as the clarity of expression, on these questions.

1. What is the name of the unit of power? (1)

    A ◯ joule   B ◯ watt

    C ◯ amp   D ◯ volt

2. An electrical circuit must contain a source of voltage. Give the name of **one** such source. (1)

    ....

3. What name do we give to the rate of flow of charge around a circuit? (1)

    ....

4. **(a)** An electric motor works at a current of 3A and a voltage of 24V. What is the electrical power of the motor? (2)

    ....

    ....

    ....

    (b) (i) 1 watt of power is the transfer of 1 joule of energy per second. How many joules of energy are transferred per second by the motor? (1)

    ....

    (ii) How many joules of energy will be transferred in 20 minutes? ($P = IV$) (2)

    ....

    ....

5. **(a)** Electricity is measured by electricity companies in units known as **kilowatt-hours**. Explain the meaning of kilowatt-hour. (1)

    ....

    (b) (i) An electric iron rated at 1.5kW is switched on for 30 minutes. How many kilowatt-hours are transferred? (1)

    ....

    (ii) What is the cost of the electricity used if 1 kilowatt-hour costs 12p? (2)

    ....

*6. Describe how you would measure the power consumption of a small low-voltage light bulb in the school laboratory. Include a drawing of the circuit you would need to set up. (6)

....

....

....

....

....

....

7. Low-energy light bulbs are often used nowadays to replace ordinary light bulbs.

(a) What is an advantage of a low-energy light bulb? (1)

....

(b) A low-energy 20W light bulb replaces one 100W light bulb.

What is the saving in power (in kW)? (2)

....

8. The energy-saving light bulb in question 7 is used for four hours a day for one year (365 days).

(a) What is the saving in kWh? (2)

....

....

(b) If 1kWh costs 10p, how much money is saved? (2)

....

....

(c) Calculate the payback time if the original cost of the light bulb was £3.90 (2)

9. **(a)** Each diagram below shows a magnet and a coil of wire. For each diagram, show the reading on the ammeter by drawing in the approximate position of the needle. (When there is no current in the coil, the needle points straight up.) The first one has been done for you. (5)

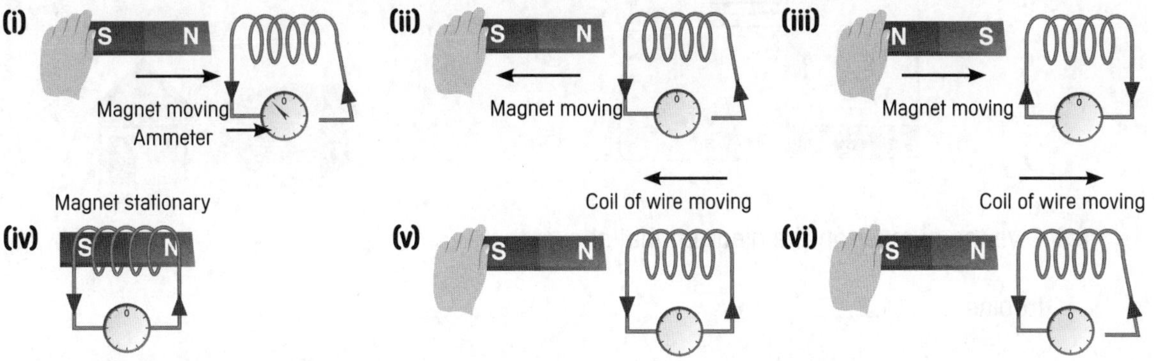

(b) In all but one of the diagrams, you get a reading on the ammeter. Why? (1)

(c) State the factors that alter the size of the current. (3)

10. Generators supply electric current that is different to the direct current supplied by batteries and cells.

(a) What name is given to the current produced by generators? (1)

(b) What is the difference between these two types of electric current?

Direct current: (1)

Alternating current: (2)

11. The diagram below shows a fossil-fuel power station.

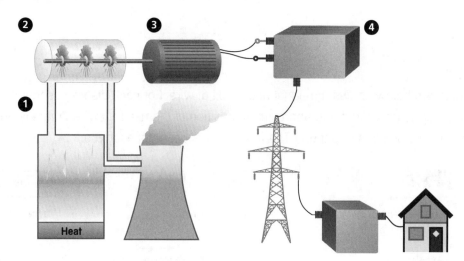

(a) Give the number on the diagram that shows the: (3)

turbine ....

boiler ....

generator ....

(b) Describe how electricity is produced. (4)

....

....

....

....

12. In order to transmit electricity in the National Grid, it is necessary to use **transformers**.

(a) What is a transformer? (2)

....

(b) Explain what a **step-up** transformer does. (1)

....

(c) Why is it necessary to use transformers? (4)

....

....

....

....

....

13. Name **one** hazard associated with the transmission of electricity. (1)

....

14. (a) Arrange the following sources of energy into two groups, depending on whether they are **renewable** or **non-renewable**. (3)

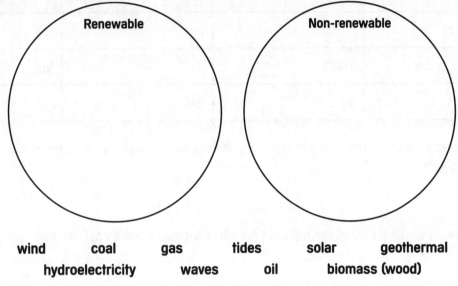

Renewable   Non-renewable

wind   coal   gas   tides   solar   geothermal
hydroelectricity   waves   oil   biomass (wood)

(b) What other name may be used to describe the non-renewable energy sources in part **(a)**? (1)

....

(c) Explain the difference between a renewable and a non-renewable energy source. (2)

....

....

....

15. (a) Explain how a wind turbine produces electricity. (3)

....

....

(b) Wind turbines are often erected in large groups, called wind farms. Why do you think this is? (2)

....

....

(c) Suggest **two** reasons why a rural community might object to a wind farm being built nearby.

(i) .... (1)

(ii) .... (1)

16. Complete the table below. (5)

Appliance	Electrical Power (W)	Voltage (V)	Current (A)
Iron	920	230	**(a)**
Kettle	2300	**(b)**	10
CD player	80	240	**(c)**
Vacuum cleaner	1400	230	**(d)**
Toaster	**(e)**	240	3

17. **(a)** A toy electric train works on a voltage of 6V at a current of 0.3A. What is the power of the train? (1)

....

(b) How much would it cost to run the train for 150 minutes, if 1kWh costs 13.4p? (2)

....

....

18. The diagram below shows a bicycle dynamo.

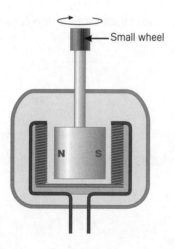

Small wheel

N   S

Explain how the dynamo makes the lamp on a bicycle light up. (4)

....

....

....

....

....

19. **(a)** At present, most of the electricity used in the UK comes from non-renewable energy sources. Why do you think that it is important for the UK to start using more renewable energy sources now? (2)

_____

_____

_____

(b) Suggest **two** possible reasons why renewable energy sources are not being used more readily.

(i) _____ (1)

(ii) _____ (1)

(c) Name **one** advantage that nearly all renewable energy sources have over non-renewable sources. (1)

_____

(Total: .... / 85)

Higher Tier

20. A step-up transformer is used at a power station to change the voltage from the National Grid from 25 000V to transmit it at 400 000V. The primary coil has 750 turns of wire on it. How many turns of wire should the secondary coil have? (3)

_____

_____

_____

(Total: .... / 3)

Questions labelled with an asterisk (*) are ones where the quality of your written communication will be assessed – you should take particular care with your spelling, punctuation and grammar, as well as the clarity of expression, on these questions.

1.   Name the type of energy that is stored in the following examples, using words from the list below.

chemical   elastic potential   gravitational potential

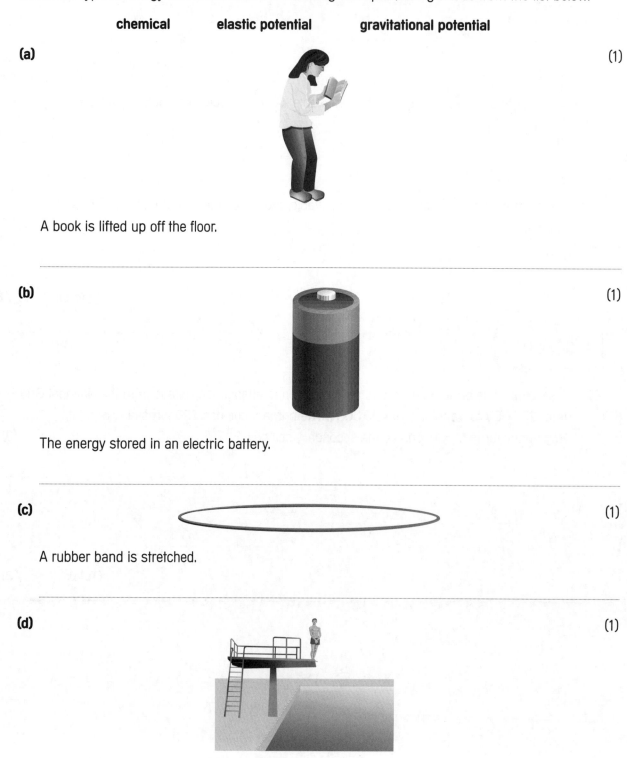

(a)   (1)

A book is lifted up off the floor.

(b)   (1)

The energy stored in an electric battery.

(c)   (1)

A rubber band is stretched.

(d)   (1)

A diver standing on the top board at a swimming pool.

(e) (1)

A lump of coal.

2. **(a)** What is meant by **kinetic energy**? (1)

(b) Give an example of something that has kinetic energy. (1)

3. Most roller coaster rides begin with the cars being winched up to the highest part of the ride by a powered lift.

Here is a basic diagram of a roller coaster.

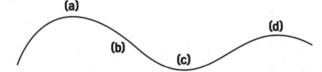

What type of energy does the car have at each of the points marked on the diagram?

(a) (1)

(b) (1)

(c) (1)

(d) (1)

4. Energy cannot be created. It can only be transferred from one form to another. What is this called? (2)

5. Complete the energy transfer described in each of the examples below.

(a) A ball is lifted up and then dropped. (1)

Gravitational potential energy transfers into

(b) An archer draws back her bow and fires an arrow. (1)

transfers into **kinetic energy**.

(c) A cyclist cycles up a hill. (1)

.... transfers into **gravitational potential energy**.

(d) A man pushes a baby buggy. (1)

.... transfers into **kinetic energy**.

6. Complete the passage below. (3)

Any electrical device can transfer .... into another form of ....

For example, an electric kettle transfers electrical energy mainly into ....

7. Describe the energy transfers that take place in the following.

(a) The blades of a wind turbine rotating. (2)

....

....

(b) A solar panel on top of a roof. (2)

....

....

(c) A solar cell in a calculator. (2)

....

....

(d) A car moving. (2)

....

....

8. An energy transfer chain is one in which there is more than one transfer of energy. Describe the energy chain that takes place when:

(a) an electric light is switched on (3)

....

....

(b) someone uses a microphone to make an announcement at school (3)

....

....

(c) a firework is set off. (3)

_____

_____

9.   Lisa likes to use her hairdryer regularly. For every 200J of energy supplied to the hairdryer, however, only 80J comes out as useful energy.

(a) What form does the useful energy take? (1)

_____

(b) For every 200J of energy supplied to the hairdryer, how many joules of **wasted** energy are there? (2)

_____

(c) What form does the waste energy take? (1)

_____

(d) Calculate the efficiency of the hairdryer. (2)

_____

_____

10.   **(a)** A hot object is situated in the middle of an enclosed room that is cooler than the object.

Describe what happens in terms of energy transfer. (2)

_____

_____

(b) The object is then moved to a second enclosed room that is warmer than the object.

Describe what happens now in terms of energy transfer. (2)

_____

_____

(c) What condition is needed for the object to stay at a constant temperature? (2)

_____

_____

11.

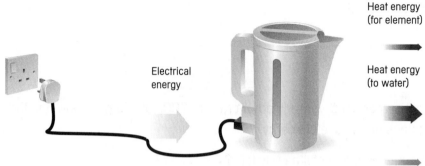

The diagram above shows an electric kettle being used to heat water.

(a) Electrical energy is supplied and is transferred to heat (or thermal) energy and one other form of energy. What is the name of this type of energy? .... (1)

(b) This energy and the thermal energy used by the element is 'wasted' energy. What does this mean? (1)

....

(c) In one second, the electrical energy supplied is 1600J.

(i) If a total of 150J is wasted, how much is used to heat the water? (1)

....

(ii) What have you assumed in your answer? (1)

....

(iii) Calculate the efficiency of the kettle. Give your answer to two significant figures. (1)

....

....

....

12. Describe the energy transfer chains that occur in the following situations.

(a) A child pulls back a catapult and releases a stone that breaks a window. (4)

....

....

....

(b) An electrical circuit with a battery is switched on. This makes a light come on which, in turn, causes a fan to switch on. (4)

....

....

....

....

*13. You are provided with the following equipment:

- a roll of matt black material

- a roll of identical material light in colour and shiny on one side

- a supply of boiling water

- a temperature sensor linked to a data logger

- a thin-walled cup.

Other equipment that you may need such as a stand and clamp are available.

Describe how you would investigate whether the nature of a surface affects the amount of energy that is radiated. What result would you expect? You may draw a labelled diagram if this helps with your description. (6)

....

....

....

....

....

(Total: .... / 68)

Higher Tier

14. A toy electric car is 40% efficient. 500J of energy is input every second.

How much useful energy is output by the car:

(a) (i) in 1 second? (2)

_____

_____

(ii) in 1 minute? (1)

_____

(b) (i) This efficiency is quite small. Suggest in what ways energy is wasted. (2)

_____

(ii) Why can the efficiency never be more than 100%? (1)

_____

(**Total:** .... / 6)

Questions labelled with an asterisk (*) are ones where the quality of your written communication will be assessed – you should take particular care with your spelling, punctuation and grammar, as well as the clarity of expression, on these questions.

1. **(a)** Give an example of an electrical **conductor**. (1)

....

(b) Give an example of an electrical **insulator**. (1)

....

(c) In terms of the flow of electricity, what is the difference between a conductor and an insulator? (1)

....

2. It is possible for an insulator to gain an electrical charge.

(a) How can this be done? (1)

....

(b) Complete this sentence.

The insulator is then said to be charged with .... (1)

3. Sven rubs a balloon on his jumper, charging it.

(a) His jumper gains a negative charge. Explain how. (2)

....

....

(b) (i) What charge does the balloon gain? (1)

....

(ii) Explain your answer. (1)

....

4. Two ebonite rods are rubbed with fur. One of these rods is suspended from a string.

(a) What will happen to the suspended rod if the other rod is moved close to it? (1)

....

(b) Explain your answer. (2)

....

....

5. Sean brings a charged ebonite rod near to a suspended and charged Perspex rod. He notices that the suspended rod moves towards the other rod. How can he explain this observation? (3)

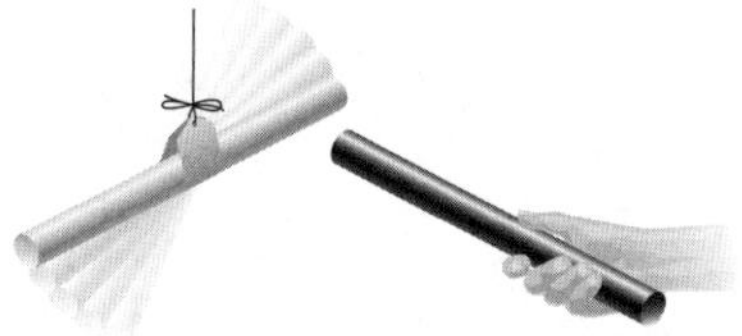

6. Salma was in her classroom, which has a nylon carpet. She found that walking over the carpet and then touching the metal radiator gave her an electric shock. Explain why this happened. (3)

7. Earthing allows excess charge to be removed from an object.

(a) Explain this in terms of the movement of electrons. (2)

(b) The diagrams below show the dome of a Van de Graaf generator. (2)

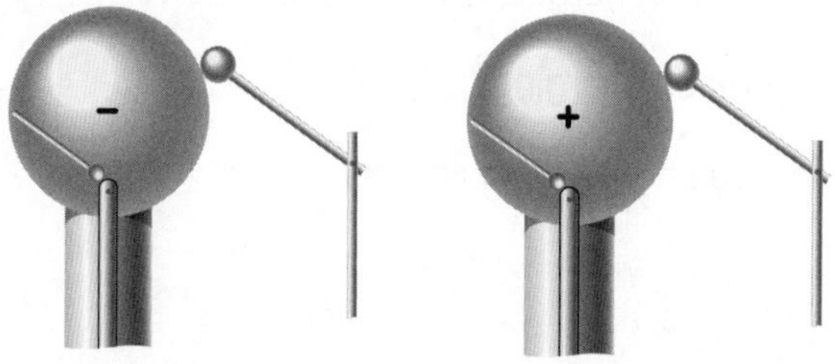

The dome on the left is negatively charged. A small sphere connected to earth touches the dome.

(i) Draw arrows to show what happens to the flow of electrons.

(ii) Do the same to the diagram on the right where the dome is positively charged.

8. Give the names of **two** examples of everyday products that make use of static electricity.

(a) .... (1)

(b) .... (1)

9. During the refuelling of planes, great care must be taken to avoid dangerous electrical discharges.

(a) How could a discharge occur? (4)

(b) Give **one** way in which this could be prevented. (1)

....

10. Calculate the charge, in coulombs, that flows when:

   (a) a current of 2A flows for 10s (1)

   ....

   (b) a current of 1.5A flows for 30s (1)

   ....

   (c) a current of 0.75A flows for 1 minute 20s. (2)

   ....

11. Clouds may become charged due to very small particles of ice rubbing against each other. In thunder clouds, the charge is greater than normal and lightning can occur.

   (a) What is lightning? (2)

   ....

   ....

   (b) The bottoms of thunder clouds gain a negative charge. Explain how lightning occurs. (4)

   ....

   ....

   ....

*12. Some buildings have a lightning conductor fixed to the outside wall. This is a copper rod that rises above the highest part of the building, with its lowest end connected to earth. Explain how this protects the building from lightning. (6)

   ....

   ....

   ....

   ....

   ....

   ....

*13. Describe the stages in the painting of a car using electrostatic charge. (6)

....

....

....

....

....

....

....

....

....

....

(Total: .... / 51)

Higher Tier

14. A charge of 3.2×10^{-2} C flows when the current in a circuit is 0.014A. How long does the charge flow for? (2)

....

....

15. What current flows if a charge of 6.72×10^{-4} C flows for 23.5 seconds? (2)

....

....

(Total: .... / 4)

Questions labelled with an asterisk (*) are ones where the quality of your written communication will be assessed – you should take particular care with your spelling, punctuation and grammar, as well as the clarity of expression, on these questions.

1. Draw the circuit diagrams in the spaces below.

    (a) A circuit with one cell and two lamps in series. (2)

    (b) A circuit with one cell and two lamps in parallel. (2)

2. The diagram below shows a simple circuit.

    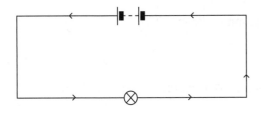

    Using the correct symbol, draw on the diagram where you would connect:

    (a) an ammeter in the circuit to measure the current (2)

    (b) a voltmeter in the circuit to measure the potential difference (voltage) across the lamp. (2)

3. The diagram below shows a circuit with two lamps in parallel. The current passing through the top lamp is 0.2A.

    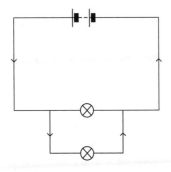

    (a) The bottom lamp is identical to the top lamp. What is the current passing through the bottom lamp? (1)

    (b) What is the total current passing through the rest of the circuit? (1)

4. A circuit has two cells connected in series with a lamp. How does the brightness of the lamp change if:

    (a) one cell is removed? _____ (1)

    (b) one cell is added so there are now three cells? _____ (1)

    (c) (i) How does the brightness of the lamp depend on the number of cells? (2)

    _____

    (ii) How does the current in the circuit depend on the size of the voltage? (2)

    _____

5. **(a) (i)** What does **resistance** mean in a circuit? (1)

    _____

    (ii) What unit is used to measure resistance? Give the full name and symbol. (1)

    _____

    (b) The resistance is increased in a circuit. How does this change the current? (1)

    _____

    (c) What component could be used in a circuit to change the resistance? (1)

    _____

6. The graph below shows how the amount of light falling on a light-dependent resistor (LDR) affects its resistance.

    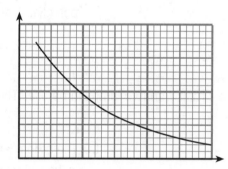

    (a) Label the axes of the graph. (2)

    (b) Explain the shape of the graph. (2)

    _____

    (c) Give **one** example of the use of an LDR. (1)

    _____

7. **(a)** Sketch and label a graph to show the relationship between resistance and temperature for a thermistor. (3)

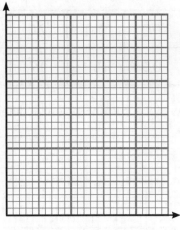

(b) In terms of resistance, thermistors are not like most electrical components, such as light bulbs. Explain why. In what ways is a thermistor like an LDR? (3)

....

....

....

8. **(a)** To calculate the potential difference across a component, what **two** things do you need to know?

(i) .... **(ii)** .... (2)

(b) In a series circuit, the reading on an ammeter is 0.6A. The total resistance is 10Ω. Calculate the potential difference supplied by the battery. (2)

....

....

9. In the circuits shown below, each cell provides a potential difference of 1.5V.

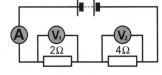 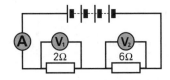 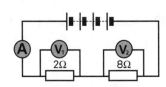

For each circuit, calculate the following: (For part **(iii)** you will need to use current = $\frac{V}{R}$)

(a) (i) p.d. supplied = ...   **(b) (i)** p.d. supplied = ...   **(c) (i)** p.d. supplied = ...

   (ii) total resistance = ...   **(ii)** total resistance = ...   **(ii)** total resistance = ...

   (iii) ammeter reading = ...   **(iii)** ammeter reading = ...   **(iii)** ammeter reading = ...

   (iv) V_1 = ...   **(iv)** V_1 = ...   **(iv)** V_1 = ...

   (v) V_2 = ... (3)   **(v)** V_2 = ... (3)   **(v)** V_2 = ... (3)

10. Josh decides to investigate how the current flowing through a filament bulb changes with the potential difference across it. He obtained the results below.

Potential Difference (V)	0.0	1.0	2.0	3.0	4.0	5.0
Current (A)	0.0	1.1	1.7	2.1	2.3	2.5

(a) On the graph paper below plot a current–potential difference graph. (4)

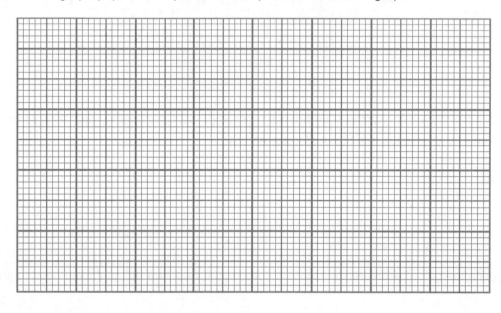

(b) (i) Describe the shape of your graph. (4)

....

....

....

....

(ii) Explain the shape of the graph. (2)

....

....

....

....

11. The graphs below show current against potential difference for different components.

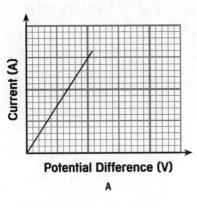

Potential Difference (V)

A

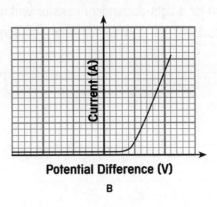

Potential Difference (V)

B

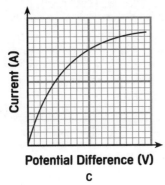

Potential Difference (V)

C

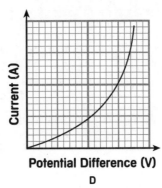

Potential Difference (V)

D

(a) Which one shows the graph for a fixed resistor? _____ (1)

(b) Which one shows the graph for a resistance that increases? _____ (1)

(c) Which one shows the graph for a diode? _____ (1)

12. An electric current passing through a wire causes it to heat up. Name a common electrical

device that makes use of this effect. _____ (1)

13. In the device you wrote as the answer to question 12, there is a transfer of energy. What is the

main energy transfer that takes place? _____ (2)

14. A similar device works on the mains voltage of 230V and draws a current of 5A.

(a) What is its power, in watts? _____ (2)

(b) How much electrical energy is transferred in:

(i) 1 second? _____ (1)

(ii) 1 minute? _____ (2)

*15. Describe how you could carry out an experiment to show the relationship between potential difference and current for a light-dependent resistor when the intensity of the light incident on the LDR is varied. You may assume that normal laboratory equipment is available. (6)

....

....

....

....

....

....

(Total: .... **/ 71)**

Higher Tier

16. **(a)** A current of 0.75A flows through a lamp. When a voltmeter is placed across the lamp to measure the potential difference, the current drops to 0.74A.

    (i) What current flows through the voltmeter? (1)

    ....

    (ii) What does this tell you about the relative size of its resistance? (2)

    ....

  (b) The voltmeter reads 3.4V.

    Calculate the resistance of the:

    (i) lamp (2)

    ....

    (ii) voltmeter. (2)

    ....

17. **(a)** In question 16, how much energy is transferred by the lamp per coulomb of charge passed? (1)

....

continued...

(b) If 15C passes through the lamp in a certain time, how much energy is transferred? (2)

18. What is the size of the current flowing in an ink-jet printer that has a power consumption of 30W, working on a mains voltage of 230V? (2)

19. A current of 4.7A is drawn by a laptop with a power output of 90W. What size voltage should the charger for the laptop provide? (2)

20. When a current flows through a resistor, there is an energy transfer.

(a) What happens to the resistor? (1)

(b) Explain, in terms of the movement of atoms and electrons, how this transfer of energy occurs. (4)

21. The energy transferred by a device is given by:

$$E = I \times V \times t$$

(a) By thinking about the definition of potential difference in terms of amount of energy transferred per unit charge, derive the relation between charge, current and time. (3)

(b) An electric kettle has a power consumption of 1100W.

    (i) How long does it take to transfer 25 000J? (1)

    (ii) Working on a mains voltage of 240V, what current does it draw? (2)

(Total: .... / 25)

Questions labelled with an asterisk (*) are ones where the quality of your written communication will be assessed – you should take particular care with your spelling, punctuation and grammar, as well as the clarity of expression, on these questions.

1. Mandy is talking to a friend, trying to explain what is meant by the velocity of a car. (1)

    A ◯ Velocity is the same as speed.

    B ◯ Velocity is speed in two different directions.

    C ◯ Velocity is speed in a certain direction.

    D ◯ Velocity is the direction of the car.

2. A distance–time graph for a person walking along a road is shown below.

    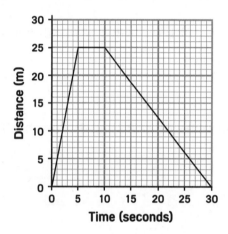

    (a) Calculate the speed:

    (i) in the first 5 seconds (2)

    _____

    (ii) in the last 20 seconds. (2)

    _____

    (b) What was the total distance walked? (1)

    _____

    (c) Describe the journey that the person takes. (3)

    _____

    _____

    _____

3. A truck is stationary at a set of traffic lights. When the lights change, it moves off and reaches a velocity of 15m/s after 30s. Calculate the acceleration of the truck. (2)

    _____

    _____

4. Study the four velocity–time graphs below.

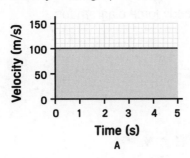

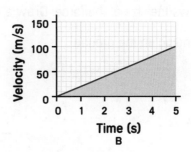

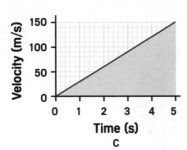

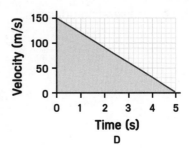

Which graphs **A**, **B**, **C** or **D** show:

(a) an object that is constantly decelerating? .... (1)

(b) an object that has zero acceleration? .... (1)

(c) an object that is constantly accelerating? .... (1)

(d) an object that is moving at a steady velocity? .... (1)

5. Calculate the acceleration shown in graph **C** of question 4. (2)

....

6. A train is moving along a track.

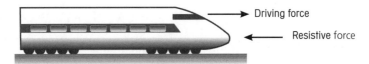

Describe the relationship between the two forces shown when: (1)

(a) the train accelerates

....

(b) the train moves at constant speed (1)

....

(c) the train slows down. (1)

....

7.   In free-body force diagrams, an arrow is used to show the direction of a force. The length of
the arrow shows the size of the force. Draw a free-body force diagram for:

(a) a man standing on the ground   (3)

(b) a hot air-balloon accelerating upwards.   (3)

8.   Calculate the weight in each of the following (taking g = 10N/kg).

(a) The mass of a girl is 45kg.   (1)

....

(b) The mass of a car is 900kg.   (1)

....

9.   A car of mass 800kg accelerates at 1.5m/s². Calculate the driving force of the car.   (2)

....

....

10. Use the formula: **acceleration = $\frac{\text{force}}{\text{mass}}$** in the following questions.

(a) A full supermarket trolley of total mass 25kg is pushed along with a resultant force of 10N.
Calculate the acceleration.   (1)

....

(b) A lorry of mass 2000kg has a driving force of 2800N. The resistive forces total 1800N.

   (i) What is the resultant driving force?   (1)

....

   (ii) Calculate the acceleration.   (1)

....

Edexcel GCSE Physics Workbook Answers

Model answers have been provided for the quality of written communication questions that are marked with an asterisk (*). The model answers would score the full 6 marks available. If you have made most of the points given in the model answer and communicated your ideas clearly, in a logical sequence with few errors in spelling, punctuation and grammar, you would get 6 marks. You will lose marks if some of the points are missing, if the answer lacks clarity and if there are serious errors in spelling, punctuation and grammar.

P1 Visible Light and the Solar System (pages 3–8)

1. Geocentric
2. Jupiter
3. Jupiter has 4 moons **(1 mark)**; Moons orbit Jupiter (not Earth) **(1 mark)**
4. Heliocentric
5. **(a)** It fitted/agreed with observations **(b)** It was thought you would feel the Earth moving
6. **(a)** Neptune lies further away **(b)** Uranus seemed out of position **(1 mark)**; another planet must be pulling on it **(1 mark)**
7.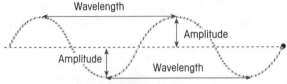
8. Number of waves/cycles **(1 mark)** per second **(1 mark)**
9. **(a)** 2Hz **(b)** 1.5m **(c)** Transverse
10. **(a)** 3Hz **(b)** 0.2m **(c)** Longitudinal
11. **(a)–(b)** Differences: **Accept any two from:** Pattern of disturbance; Travel at different speeds; Longitudinal needs medium but (most) transverse do not **(c)** Similarity: Both carry energy
12. 340 **(1 mark)** m/s **(1 mark)**
13. 0.25m/s
14. **(a)** Bends/refracts/changes direction away from the normal **(b)** Reflects (back into glass)
15. **(a)** Naked/unaided eye **(b)** Photography **(c)** Telescope/binoculars **(in any order)**
16.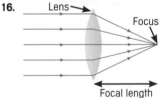
   (1 mark for each correct label)
17. Hold lens up to distant object **(1 mark)**; Move screen until a sharp image is obtained **(1 mark)**; Measure distance from lens to screen **(1 mark)**; Screen and object on opposite sides of lens **(1 mark)**
18. **(a)–(b)** Eyepiece, Objective **(2 marks)**
19. Light from a distant object or source strikes the large/parabolic mirror **(1 mark)**, reflected to the small/flat mirror **(1 mark)**, then into the lens/eyepiece and into the eye **(1 mark)**
20. Naked eye **Advantage:** Easy/no equipment needed; **Disadvantage:** Can't see much/depends on eyesight; Photography **Advantage:** Permanent record; **Disadvantage:** Stars, etc. seen as streaks/must use tripod. Telescope **Advantage:** More can be seen; **Disadvantage:** (More) difficult to use **(1 mark for each correct line)**
21. **(a)** Gathers light (from distant object) **(b)** Magnifies image (produced by objective)
*22. A simple telescope has an objective lens, which gathers light from a distant source. An image (of an object) is produced within the focal length of the eyepiece. The eyepiece magnifies the image. A reflecting telescope gathers much more light and uses mirrors to reflect the light to form an image. It uses mirrors, not lenses. Large mirrors are easier and cheaper to make than large lenses.

23. **(a)–(c)**
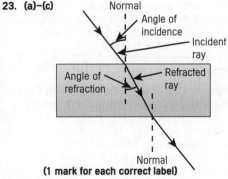
   (1 mark for each correct label)
24. It slows down.
25. **(a)** $\text{Frequency} = \dfrac{\text{wave speed}}{\text{wavelength}} = \dfrac{300\,000\,000}{252}$ **(1 mark)**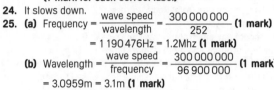
   $= 1\,190\,476\text{Hz} = 1.2\text{Mhz}$ **(1 mark)**
   (b) $\text{Wavelength} = \dfrac{\text{wave speed}}{\text{frequency}} = \dfrac{300\,000\,000}{96\,900\,000}$ **(1 mark)**
   $= 3.0959\text{m} = 3.1\text{m}$ **(1 mark)**

P1 The Electromagnetic Spectrum (pages 9–12)

1. C **should be ticked**.
2.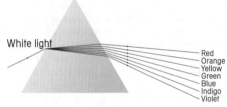
   (7 correct = 4 marks; 5–6 correct = 3 marks; 3–4 correct = 2 marks; 1–2 correct = 1 mark)
3. Gamma rays; X-rays; Ultraviolet; (visible light); Infrared; Microwaves; Radio waves **(1 mark for correct order either side of visible light)**
4. **(a)** False **(b)** True **(c)** False **(d)** False
5. **(a)** Microwaves **(b)** Ultraviolet **(c)** Infrared **(d)** Ultraviolet
6. Damage to surface cells (skin) and eyes **(1 mark)** leading to skin cancer and eye conditions **(1 mark)**
7. Gamma rays
8. **(a) (i)** Observe internal structure (bodies/metal)/airport security scanner **(ii)** Kill/damage cells/cause cancer **(b)** Different wavelength/frequency
9. The equipment uses infrared sensors **(1 mark)**; these detect infrared/thermal energy/heat energy **(1 mark)**; which is emitted from a person at night or when a person hides **(1 mark)**; or when they are trapped in a building **(1 mark)**
10. (William) Herschel
11. Part of body with fracture is placed in front of photographic plate **(1 mark)**, exposed to X-rays **(1 mark)**, X-rays pass through fracture/soft tissues **(1 mark)** but are absorbed by bones leaving an image of the bones and any cracks on the plate **(1 mark)**
12. **(a)** They penetrate the food to melt 3 or 4cm of ice **(1 mark)**, as the food is rotated the radiation spreads out evenly defrosting it thoroughly **(1 mark)** **(b)** They cannot penetrate (food)/only absorbed by surface **(1 mark)**; Surface/top layer starts cooking, rest of food still frozen **(1 mark)**
13. **(a)** They remove outer electron/s from atom/s **(1 mark)** they leave atom positively charged **(1 mark)** **(b) Accept any two from:** They damage(living) cells; Kill normal cells; Cause mutation
14. **(a)** Microwaves **(b)** Can cause internal heating of (body) tissue **(1 mark)**; Damages/kills cells **(1 mark)**
15. **(a)** Yes, microwaves can heat beneath the tissue surface **(1 mark)** so they may heat the brain **(1 mark)**

(b) No, the temperature increase from microwaves/a mobile phone is small **(1 mark)** compared to the brain's natural temperature fluctuations **(1 mark)**. **Or** Yes, even small temperature fluctuations from a mobile **(1 mark)** may be dangerous, we don't know **(1 mark)**

16. **Herschel** measured temperature difference of parts of visible spectrum with (row of) thermometers **(1 mark)**; temperature increased (a lot) beyond red end **(1 mark)** *or* **Ritter** studied reaction of silver chloride in light/visible spectrum reaction **(1 mark)**; increased (a lot) beyond violet end **(1 mark)**

P1 Waves and the Universe (pages 13–18)

1. **(a)** Mercury **(b)** Earth **(c)** Mars **(d)** Jupiter **(e)** Uranus **(f)** Neptune **(6 correct = 3 marks; 4-5 correct = 2 marks; 2-3 correct = 1 mark)**
2. **C should be ticked**.
3. Moon, Planet, Sun, Solar System, Galaxy, Universe
4. **(a)** Jupiter **(b)** Mercury **(c)** Mercury **(d)** Venus/Mars
5. **(a)** Ball of hot gas **(b)** Collection of stars **(c)** Milky Way
6. **(a) Accept any one from:** Radio; Infrared; Ultraviolet; X-rays; Gamma rays
   (b) Accept any one from: Ultraviolet; X-rays; Gamma rays
7. Evolution of/more and more **(1 mark)** galaxies **(1 mark)**
8. (Extremely) dense **(1 mark)** rotating star **(1 mark)**, neutron star/pulsar **(1 mark)**, sends out signal like lighthouse **(1 mark)**
9. Estimate age of Universe **(1 mark)**; Rate of expansion of Universe **(1 mark)**
10. **(a)** Sending spaceships to collect data **(b)** Looking for radio signals
11. **(a)** Safer **(b)** Journey too long for astronauts
12. (Programme) to search for radio signals from aliens **(1 mark)**; Stands for Search for Extra Terrestrial Intelligence **(1 mark)**
13. Nebula, main sequence star, red giant, white dwarf
14. When fusion occurs in stars, hydrogen nuclei join together to form helium **(1 mark)**, light and heat energy are produced **(1 mark)** stars in a stable state are known as the main sequence **(1 mark)**
15. **(a)** The Steady State Theory asserts that although the Universe is expanding, it does not change its appearance over time **(1 mark)**; it has no beginning and no end **(1 mark)**
    (b) Universe started (about) 15 billion years ago **(1 mark)** in a huge explosion **(1 mark)**; Universe is (continually) expanding **(1 mark)**
    (c) Red-shift (of light from galaxies) **(1 mark)** cosmic/microwave background radiation **(1 mark)**
16. Sun 400 times bigger **(1 mark)** but 400 times further away **(1 mark)**
17. Very little UV is detected on the Earth, most doesn't penetrate the atmosphere **(1 mark)**, it is absorbed, by the ozone layer, before reaching the Earth, or it is scattered before reaching the Earth **(1 mark)**
18. **(a)** Red giant stage A white dwarf
        red supergiant stage B supernova → neutron star
        (1 mark for each correct circle)
    (b) Collapses **(1 mark)**, under its own gravity **(1 mark)**
    (c) Shrinks rapidly **(1 mark)** explodes **(1 mark)**, releases (huge) energy, dust and gas **(1 mark)**
19. **(a)** Light from (distant) galaxies **(1 mark)**, shifted to red (end of spectrum/lower frequency) **(1 mark)**, (light) source moving away **(1 mark)**, this shows that galaxies are moving away from us and so the universe is expanding **(1 mark)**
    (b) (Steady State) says new matter continually created (to fill space) **(1 mark)** which contravenes conservation of energy/matter **(1 mark)** it can't explain cosmic background radiation **(1 mark)**
20. **(a)** It is moving away (from Earth)
    (b) (i) It is moving away **(1 mark)** at faster rate (than A). **(1 mark)**
        (ii) It is more distant
    (c) The more distant the galaxy **(1 mark)** the faster the expansion **(1 mark)**

P1 Waves and the Earth (pages 19–22)

1. Vibrates; Longitudinal; Audible range; Ultrasound; Infrasound
2. **Accept any two from:** Sonar; Communication between animals; Foetal scans
3. **Accept any one from:** Elephant; Whale; Rhino; etc.
4. Seismic
5. P and S
6. Volcanic eruptions/volcanoes
7. A wave caused by underwater disturbance/earthquake/volcano
8. Earth's plates **(1 mark)** do not move in regular patterns **(1 mark)**
9. **(a)** Ultrasound is emitted from the boat and hits the seabed **(1 mark)**; it reflects from the seabed and is detected by equipment on the boat **(1 mark)**; the depth can be calculated from the length of time between the signal being emitted and received **(1 mark)**
    (b) Depth = 1500 × 1 **(1 mark)** = 1500m **(1 mark)**.
*10. The plates move due to convection currents in the Earth's mantle. As the plates move, they slide past each other. This movement is not smooth and causes the plates to get stuck. As a result, pressure builds up and an earthquake is caused by the sudden release of this pressure.
11. **(a)** Vibrations make (heavy) mass move **(1 mark)** drum rotates **(1 mark)** vibrations recorded on drum/paper **(1 mark)**
    (b) The time taken for waves to arrive at each seismometer **(1 mark)**; are compared **(1 mark)**
12. P waves are longitudinal; S waves are transverse **(1 mark)** P waves travel through solid and liquids; S waves travel through solids only **(1 mark)**
13. **(a)** Secondary waves (S waves) / Primary waves (P waves)

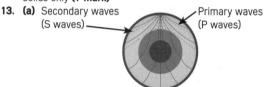

    P and S waves drawn curved **(1 mark)**
    Only P waves drawn passing through centre/core **(1 mark)**
    P waves refracted at (different) boundaries **(1 mark)**
    (b) (i) Both P and S will reach Station Z **(1 mark)**; Both can travel through solids **(1 mark)**
        (ii) Only P waves with reach Station Y **(1 mark)**; P waves can travel through liquid core **(1 mark)**

P1 Generation and Transmission of Electricity (pages 23–29)

1. **B should be ticked**.
2. Cell/battery
3. Current
4. **(a)** 3 × 24 **(1 mark)** = 72W **(1 mark)**
    (b) (i) 72 **(ii)** 72 × 20 × 60 **(1 mark)** = 86400 **(1 mark)**
5. **(a)** 1 kilowatt of (electrical) power used (by a device) in 1 hour
    (b) (i) 0.75 **(ii)** 0.75 × 12 **(1 mark)** = 9p **(1 mark)**
*6.

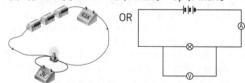

    A school power pack, a supply set on d.c, a number of cells or batteries are used as the power source. The ammeter is placed in the series and the voltmeter is placed in parallel with the lamp or light bulb. Record the ammeter reading. Record the voltmeter reading. The power (of the lamp) = ammeter reading × voltmeter reading.
7. **(a)** Saves money/energy **(b)** $\frac{(100-20)}{1000}$ **(1 mark)** = 0.08kW **(1 mark)**
8. **(a)** 0.08 × 4 × 365 **(1 mark)** = 116.8kWh **(1 mark)**
    (b) 116.8 × 10p **(1 mark)** = £11.68 **(1 mark)**
    (c) $\frac{£3.90}{£11.68}$ **(1 mark)** = 0.33 years/4 months **(1 mark)**

9. (a) (ii)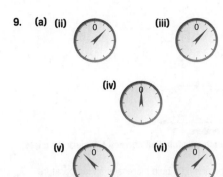
(iii)
(iv)
(v)
(vi)

(b) There is a current in the coil if there is a magnet or coil moving (relative to each other)
(c) Speed of movement **(1 mark)**; Strength of magnet **(1 mark)**; Number of turns **(1 mark)**

10. (a) Alternating current
(b) Direct current: current flows in one direction **(1 mark)**; Alternating current: current changes direction **(1 mark)** (continually) **(1 mark)**

11. (a) Turbine = 2; Boiler = 1; Generator = 3
(b) The boiler burns fuel **(1 mark)**; Heats the water **(1 mark)**; The steam drives the turbine **(1 mark)**; The generator turns **(1 mark)**

12. (a) A device that changes current/voltage **(1 mark)**; Uses an alternating voltage/current **(1 mark)**
(b) It increases voltage.
(c) The voltage transmitted must be high **(1 mark)** to reduce heat loss **(1 mark)**; A step-up transformer increases voltage (at a power station) **(1 mark)**; A step-down transformer reduces voltage for users **(1 mark)**

13. Overhead power lines/sub-stations

14. (a) Renewable: wind, tides, solar, geothermal, hydroelectricity waves, biomass; Non-renewable: coal, gas, oil
(3 marks, subtract 1 for each incorrect answer)
(b) Fossil fuels
(c) Renewable: can be replaced (or similar words but **not** can be 're-used') **(1 mark)**; Non-renewable: can't be replaced/ will run out **(1 mark)**

15. (a) Wind turns blades **(1 mark)** blades turn turbine **(1 mark)** turbine turns generator **(1 mark)**
(b) More electricity can be generated **(1 mark)** in one place **(1 mark)**
(c) (i) and (ii) **Accept any two from:** Visual pollution; Noise pollution; Danger to birds

16. (a) 4 (b) 230 (c) 0.33 (d) 6.1 (e) 720

17. (a) 1.8W (b) $\frac{1.8}{1000}$ × 2.5 × 13.4 **(1 mark)** = 0.06p **(1 mark)**

18. The pedals/wheels of the bicycle turn. This makes the small wheel of the dynamo rotate **(1 mark)**, this is connected to a (cylindrical) magnet, so that the magnet also rotates **(1 mark)**, a current is induced in the coil surrounding the magnet **(1 mark)**, this current passes through the lamp making it light up **(1 mark)**

19. (a) Non-renewable will run out; **(1 mark)** Non-renewable contributes to global warming **(1 mark)**
(b) (i) and (ii) **Accept any two from:** Renewable is less efficient; (Generally) less reliable; Start-up costs high; Visual pollution; Interference with wild life
(c) They are free/don't cost anything or don't have to be mined/ extracted

20. Turns ratio = $\frac{400\,000}{25\,000}$ **(1 mark)** turns ratio × 750 **(1 mark)** 12 000 turns **(1 mark)**

P1 Energy and the Future (pages 30–36)

1. (a) Gravitational potential (b) Chemical (c) Elastic potential (d) Gravitational potential (e) Chemical

2. (a) Energy that something moving has (b) Anything moving, e.g. a person running

3. (a) Gravitational potential (b) Kinetic and Gravitational potential (c) Kinetic (d) Kinetic and Gravitational potential

4. (The principle of) the conservation **(1 mark)** of energy **(1 mark)**

5. (a) Kinetic energy (b) Elastic potential energy (c) Kinetic energy (d) Chemical energy (in muscles)

6. Electrical energy **(1 mark)**; Energy **(1 mark)**; Heat/thermal energy **(1 mark)**

7. (a) Kinetic to electrical (b) Light to heat/thermal (c) Light to electrical (d) Chemical (in fuel) to kinetic

8. (a) Electrical to heat/thermal to light (b) Sound to electrical to sound (c) Chemical to kinetic to light and heat

9. (a) Heat/thermal (b) 200 – 80 **(1 mark)** = 120J **(1 mark)**
(c) Sound (d) $\frac{80}{200}$ × 100% **(1 mark)** = 40% **(1 mark)**

10. (a) The object radiates thermal energy **(1 mark)** and then it cools down **(1 mark)**
(b) The object absorbs thermal energy **(1 mark)** and the object warms up **(1 mark)**
(c) Average rate of energy/power absorbed **(1 mark)** = average rate of energy/power radiated **(1 mark)**

11. (a) Sound (b) Not used to heat water (c) (i) 1450J
(ii) Conservation of energy (iii) $\frac{1450}{1600}$ = 91%

12. (a) Chemical (in child's muscles) **(1 mark)** to elastic potential **(1 mark)** to kinetic **(1 mark)** to sound + thermal **(1 mark)**
(b) Chemical (battery) **(1 mark)** to electrical **(1 mark)** to thermal + light **(1 mark)** to kinetic + sound **(1 mark)**

*13. Firstly cover the cup in the matt black material and fix the temperature sensor in a clamp inside of the cup. Pour in a set volume of boiling water and record the temperature using the data logger at set periods of time for a fixed time (i.e. 1 minute). Now remove the matt black material and cover the same cup with the light material shiny side inwards. Fill the cup with the same volume of boiling water and repeat the measurements with the temperature probe for the same period of time. One would expect the temperature of the water in the matt black cup to have decreased more.

14. (a) (i) 500 × 0.4 **(1 mark)** = 200J **(1 mark)** (ii) 12 000J
(b) (i) Sound, heat/thermal (ii) Principle of conservation of energy

P2 Static and Current Electricity (pages 37–40)

1. (a) Any metal (b) Most non-metals (c) Conductors allow electricity to flow, insulators do not

2. (a) Friction/rubbing with another insulator (b) Static electricity

3. (a) Electrons **(1 mark)** go from balloon to jumper **(1 mark)**
(b) (i) Positive (ii) Fewer electrons/less negative charge on balloon

4. (a) Repels/moves away
(b) Both (rods) have the same charge **(1 mark)** same charges repel **(1 mark)**

5. Perspex rod has opposite charge **(1 mark)** to ebonite rod **(1 mark)** opposite charges attract **(1 mark)**

6. Shoes rub on carpet **(1 mark)** shoes/Salma gains charge **(1 mark)** charge flows to (metal) radiator **(1 mark)**

7. (a) Electrons flow/move **(1 mark)** from one object to another **(1 mark)**
(b)
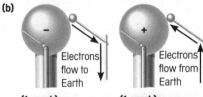

Electrons flow to Earth

Electrons flow from Earth

(1 mark) **(1 mark)**

8. (a)-(b) **Accept any two from:** Laser printer; Photocopier; Xerox copier; Paint sprayer; Insecticide sprayer; Computer memory; Removal of smoke from factory chimneys; Air ionisers; Defibrillators

9. (a) Fuel gains electrons (from pipe)/pipe loses electrons (to fuel) **(1 mark)**, so the pipe becomes positively charged, the fuel becomes negatively charged **(1 mark)**, this results in a potential difference/voltage, between the pipe and the fuel **(1 mark)**, this could lead to a discharge/spark/explosion **(1 mark)**
(b) Tank can be earthed/tanker and plane can be linked with (copper) conductor

10. (a) 20C (b) 45C (c) 0.75 × 80 **(1 mark)** = 60C **(1 mark)**

11. **(a)** (Atmospheric) discharge **(1 mark)** of static electricity **(1 mark)**
(b) Separation of charges builds up **(1 mark)**; Cloud induces positive charge on ground **(1 mark)**; Potential difference between ground and cloud **(1 mark)**; Electrons jump from cloud to ground **(1 mark)**

*12. The conductor is the tallest, positively charged object on the building. A (thunder) cloud induces a positive charge on the top of the conductor. The conductor provides an easier path for charges to flow because it is made of copper and copper has a low electrical resistance. So the conductor provides a path for the charges to flow to Earth, rather than through the building.

*13. Paint is forced through a nozzle. This breaks it in to very small droplets. The small drops of paint are made to be electrically charged, thereby repelling each other; this causes them to spread themselves evenly as they exit the spray nozzle. The object being painted is charged oppositely or grounded. The paint is then attracted to the object giving a more even coat than wet spray painting.

14. $\dfrac{3.2 \times 10^{-2}}{0.014}$ **(1 mark)** = 2.3s **(1 mark)**

15. $\dfrac{6.72 \times 10^{-4}}{23.5}$ **(1 mark)** = 2.86×10^{-5}A **(1 mark)**

P2 Controlling and Using Electric Current (pages 41–47)

1. **(a)**
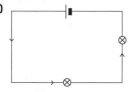
(1 mark for correct symbols, 1 mark for correct positions)
(b)
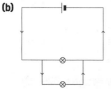
(1 mark for correct symbols, 1 mark for correct positions)

2.
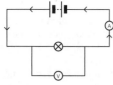
(a) **(1 mark for correct symbol, 1 mark for correct position - ammeter can be anywhere in the line of the circuit)**
(b) **(1 mark for correct symbol, 1 mark for correct position)**

3. **(a)** 0.2A **(b)** 0.4A
4. **(a)** Dimmer/less bright
(b) Brighter
(c) **(i)** Number of cells increase **(1 mark)**, brightness increases **(1 mark)**
(ii) Voltage increases **(1 mark)**, current increases **(1 mark)**
5. **(a)** **(i)** How hard it is for current to flow
(ii) ohms, Ω
(b) Reduces/gets smaller
(c) Variable resistor
6. **(a)**
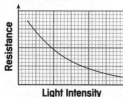
(1 mark for each axis labelled correctly)
(b) As light intensity/light level increases **(1 mark)** resistance decreases **(1 mark)**
(c) **Accept any one from:** Automatic light detector; Control exposure in camera; In a circuit to switch on/off a light, etc.

7. **(a)**
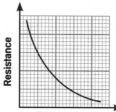
(1 mark for each axis labelled correctly, 1 mark for curve as shown)
(b) The resistance of a light bulb increases as temperature increases **(1 mark)**, the resistance of a thermistor decreases as temperature increases **(1 mark)**, this is similar to the way the resistance of an LDR changes/varies or the graph looks the same. But its resistance changes/varies with light (intensity), not temperature **(1 mark)**
8. **(a)** **(i)** Current **(ii)** Resistance **(any order)**
(b) 0.6×10 **(1 mark)** = 6V **(1 mark)**
9. **(a)** **(i)** 3V **(ii)** 6Ω **(iii)** 0.5A **(iv)** 1V **(v)** 2V
(b) **(i)** 6V **(ii)** 8Ω **(iii)** 0.75A **(iv)** 1.5V **(v)** 4.5V
(c) **(i)** 6V **(ii)** 10Ω **(iii)** 0.6A **(iv)** 1.2V **(v)** 4.8V
(**(a)–(c)** 5 correct = 3 marks; 3–4 correct = 2 marks; 1–2 correct = 1 mark)
10. **(a)**
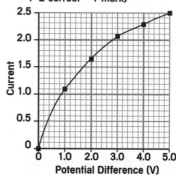
Current (A) on y-axis **(1 mark)**; Potential difference(V) on x-axis **(1 mark)**; Correct plotting **(1 mark)**; Smooth curve **(1 mark)**
(b) **(i)** Curve **(1 mark)** as p.d. increases current increases **(1 mark)** at a smaller rate/current tends to maximum **(1 mark)** as filament heats up **(1 mark)**
(ii) Resistance increases **(1 mark)** as the temperature of the bulb increases **(1 mark)**
11. **(a)** A **(b)** C **(c)** B
12. **Accept any one from:** Hairdryer; Immersion heater; Kettle; Toaster; Light bulb, etc.
13. Electrical **(1 mark)** to thermal/heat **(1 mark)**
14. **(a)** 230×5 **(1 mark)** = 1150W **(1 mark)**
(b) **(i)** 1150J
(ii) 1150×60 **(1 mark)** = 69 000J **(1 mark)**
*15. Set up a circuit with an ammeter in series with an LDR. A voltmeter must be connected in parallel with the LDR. With the room blacked out or darkened, a variable brightness lamp is directed at the LDR and the light intensity varied. For each setting of the lamp, the potential difference and current are recorded. Finally, plot a graph of current against potential difference.
16. **(a)** **(i)** 0.01A **(ii)** (Much) bigger **(1 mark)** 74 times bigger **(1 mark)**
(b) **(i)** R (lamp): $\dfrac{3.4}{0.74}$ **(1 mark)** = 4.6Ω **(1 mark)**
(ii) R(voltmeter): $\dfrac{3.4}{0.01}$ **(1 mark)** = 340Ω **(1 mark)**
17. **(a)** 3.4J **(b)** 15×3.4 **(1 mark)** = 51J **(1 mark)**
18. $\dfrac{30}{230}$ **(1 mark)** = 0.13A **(1 mark)**
19. $\dfrac{90}{4.7}$ **(1 mark)** = 19V **(1 mark)**
20. **(a)** It gets hot/becomes heated
(b) Electrons collide **(1 mark)** with ions **(1 mark)** in lattice **(1 mark)**; Energy is transferred from electrons to ions **(1 mark)**

21. **(a)** $V = \dfrac{E}{Q}$ **(1 mark)** $E = I \times \dfrac{E}{Q} \times t$ **(1 mark)** $Q = I \times t$ **(1 mark)**

    (b) **(i)** $\dfrac{25\,000}{1100} = 22.7 = 23\text{s}$ (to 2sf)

       (ii) $\dfrac{1100}{240}$ **(1 mark)** $= 4.6\text{A} =$ **(1 mark)**

P2 Motion and Forces (pages 48–53)

1. C **should be ticked.**

2. **(a)** **(i)** $\dfrac{25}{5}$ **(1 mark)** $= 5\text{m/s}$ **(1 mark)** **(ii)** $\dfrac{25}{20}$ **(1 mark)**

       1.25m/s **(1 mark)**

    (b) 50m
    (c) Walks at steady speed (for 5s) **(1 mark)**, stops (for 5s) **(1 mark)**, then walks back at slower speed (for 20s) **(1 mark)**

3. $\dfrac{(15-0)}{30}$ **(1 mark)** $= 0.5\text{m/s}^2$ **(1 mark)**

4. **(a)** D **(b)** A **(c)** B and C **(d)** A

5. $\dfrac{150}{5}$ **(1 mark)** $= 30\text{m/s}^2$ **(1 mark)**

6. **(a)** Driving force is bigger than the resistive force
    (b) Forces are equal
    (c) Driving force is less than the resistive force

7. **(a)**

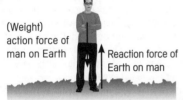

(Weight) action force of man on Earth

Reaction force of Earth on man

(1 mark for reaction force of man on Earth up arrow and 1 mark for the weight down arrow. 1 mark for arrows being the same length.)

    (b) Upthrust (due to the displacement of air surrounding balloon)

(1 mark for up arrow labelled upthrust, 1 mark for down arrow labelled weight, 1 mark for up arrow longer than down arrow, credit to be given if downward force air resistance is labelled)

Weight

8. **(a)** 450N **(b)** 9000N

9. 800×1.5 **(1 mark)** $= 1200\text{N}$ **(1 mark)**

10. **(a)** 0.4m/s^2 **(b)** **(i)** 1000N **(ii)** 0.5m/s^2

11. D **should be ticked.**

12. **(a)** **(i)** Accelerates; because of weight/gravity
       (ii) Acceleration less because of air resistance
       (iii) Acceleration even less as air resistance increases
       (iv) No acceleration; weight = air resistance; reaches terminal velocity
    (b) Parachute opens
    (c) **(i)** Speed decreases since air resistance bigger
       (ii) Speed further decreases so air resistance less
       (iii) Steady speed/no acceleration; weight = air resistance; reaches terminal velocity
       (iv) Speed zero – lands on ground

*13. The runway needs to be raised until the trolley moves at constant speed or velocity. This means there is no (zero) acceleration, which implies no (zero) resultant force acting on the trolley. Since the runway has friction, raising the slope eliminates the need to take friction into account. Any extra force on the trolley will then be the accelerating force. Raising the slope would not be necessary if the runway was smooth/friction free (but that is unlikely).

14. $v = \dfrac{90 \times 1000}{3600} = 25\text{m/s}$ **(1 mark)** $u = v - a \times t$ **(1 mark)**

    $25 - 2 \times 5$ **(1 mark)** $= 15\text{m/s}$ **(1 mark)**

15. $m = F/a = \dfrac{20\,000}{0.8} = 25\,000\text{kg}$

16. **(a)** 3000N
    (b) Resultant = 1000N **(1 mark)** 1m/s^2 **(1 mark)**
    (c) $v = 30 + 1 \times 20$ **(1 mark)** $= 50\text{m/s}$ **(1 mark)**

17. **(a)** $\dfrac{25}{(5 \times 60)}$ **(1 mark)** $= 0.083\text{m/s}^2$ **(1 mark)**
    (b) $25 \times 5 \times 60$ **(1 mark)** $= 7500\text{m}$ **(1 mark)**
    (c) $0.5 \times 300 \times 25 + 7500 + 0.5 \times 20 \times 60 \times 25$ **(1 mark)** $= 26\,250\text{m}$ **(1 mark)**
    (d) $\dfrac{25}{(20 \times 60)}$ **(1 mark)** $= 0.021\text{m/s}^2$ **(1 mark)**
    (e) $\dfrac{26\,250}{(30 \times 60)}$ **(1 mark)** $= 14.6\text{m/s}$ **(1 mark)**

P2 Momentum, Energy, Work and Power (pages 54–59)

1. **(a)** Thinking distance **(b)** Braking distance

2. C **should be ticked.**

3. **(a)** Time from seeing child **(1 mark)** to applying brakes **(1 mark)**
    (b) **(i)** and **(ii)** **Accept any two from:** Drinking alcohol; Taking drugs; Being distracted; Using mobile

4. B **Should be ticked.**

5. **(a)** Mass **(b)** Velocity **(any order)**

6. **(a)** 1000×20 **(1 mark)** $= 20\,000\text{kg m/s}$ **(1 mark)**
    (b) $-20\,000\text{kg m/s}$

7. Total mass 340kg **(1 mark)** $\dfrac{8500}{340}$ **(1 mark)** $= 25\text{m/s}$ **(1 mark)**

8. **(a)** (Total) momentum before collision = (Total) momentum after collision **(b)** **(i)** $800 \times 20 + 800 \times 30$ **(1 mark)** $40\,000\text{kg m/s}$ **(1 mark)** **(ii)** $40\,000\text{kg m/s}$

9. 150×1500 **(1 mark)** $= 225\,000\text{J}$ **(1 mark)**

10. **(a)** 50×1.8 **(1 mark)** $= 90\text{J}$ **(1 mark)** **(b)** 90J **(c)** Energy transferred = work done

11. **(a)** $50\,000 \times 30$ **(1 mark)** $= 1\,500\,000\text{J}$ **(1 mark)**
    (b) $\dfrac{1\,500\,000}{20}$ **(1 mark)** $75\,000\text{W}/75\text{kW}$ **(1 mark)**

12. **(a)** Energy gained by lifting object above ground/$m \times g \times h$ with m, g, h explained **(b)** **(i)-(ii)** **Accept any answer where the object is above ground, e.g.** Diver on board; Book on bookshelf, etc.

13. $50 \times 10 \times 5$ **(1 mark)** $= 2500\text{J}$ **(1 mark)**

14. **(a)** $0.4 \times 10 \times 8$ **(1 mark)** $= 32\text{J}$ **(1 mark)** **(b)** Transfers to KE

15. **(a)** and **(b)** **Accept any two examples where object is moving, e.g.** Moving car; Running man, etc.

16. $0.5 \times 2000 \times 20^2$ **(1 mark)** $= 400\,000\text{J}$ **(1 mark)**

17. **(a)** (iv) **(b)** (iii) **(c)** (i) **(d)** (ii)

*18. Attach a newton meter to the block or attach a mass holder by string (over a pulley) to the block. Pull the block along the surface or place masses on the holder to make the block move. Make sure the block moves steadily. Record the force (in newtons). Repeat this to get an average force. Change the surface to make it rougher or smoother and repeat the experiment.

19. Air bags increase time of stopping **(1 mark)** rate of change of momentum less **(1 mark)** force acting less **(1 mark)**

20. **(a)** 20m/s **(b)** 20m **(c)** 4s **(d)** 60m

21. **(a)** $10^4 \times 10 \times 120$ **(1 mark)** $= 1.2 \times 10^7$ J/12MJ **(1 mark)**
    (b) $\dfrac{1.2 \times 10^7}{200}$ **(1 mark)** $= 60\,000\text{W}/60\text{kW}$ **(1 mark)**

22. D **should be ticked.**

23. Change in momentum = $F \times t$ **(1 mark)** 2000×0.45 **(1 mark)** $= 900$ **(1 mark)** kg m/s **(1 mark)**

24. **(a)** $750 \times 20 - 750 \times 5$ **(1 mark)** $= 11\,250\text{kg m/s}$ **(1 mark)**
    (b) Rate of change of momentum $= \dfrac{11\,250}{5}$ **(1 mark)** force $= 2250\text{N}$ **(1 mark)**

25. **(a)** Work done = KE
    (b) WD $= F \times d$ **(1 mark)** KE $= 0.5 \times m \times v^2$ **(1 mark)** $Fd = 0.5mv^2$ **(1 mark)** F and m are constant, therefore d proportional to v^2 **(1 mark)**
    (c) $\dfrac{0.5 \times 5000 \times 25^2}{10\,000}$ **(1 mark)** $= 156\text{m}$ **(1 mark)**

*26. The energy to stop the vehicle is equal to its kinetic energy. The energy is the force times the distance to stop the car. Connor is right that there is more energy if it goes faster, since faster means greater kinetic energy. Habiba is right that energy is not proportional to the velocity, since kinetic energy is proportional to the square of the velocity, so that energy or the stopping distance is also proportional to the square of the velocity. But Habiba says the stopping distance is 'much more' (at greater speeds) which isn't clear.

P2 Nuclear Fission and Nuclear Fusion (pages 60–65)

1. **(a)** Proton **(b)** Neutron **(c)** Electron
2. **(a)** (Element with) same number of protons **(1 mark)**, different number of neutrons **(1 mark) (b) (i)** 27, 27 **(ii)** 33, 32 **(iii)** 27, 27 **(1 mark for each correct row)**
3. A = mass number/number or protons + neutrons; Z = atomic number/number of protons/electrons
4. $^{60}_{27}Co$ $^{59}_{27}Co$
5. (Unstable) nucleus that splits/disintegrates/emits radiation
6. **(a)** (i), (iii), (vii) **(b)** (i), (v), (vi) **(c)** (i), (ii), (iv)
7. **(a)** Beta and gamma **(b)** Aluminium or lead **(c)** Gamma
8. **(a) Accept any three from:** Radiation collides with atoms; Atoms lose electron/s; Atoms become charged; Charged atoms are called ions
   (b) Alpha
9. Nuclear fission: fission-splitting **(1 mark)** of large/heavy nucleus **(1 mark)**; Nuclear fusion: Fusion-joining **(1 mark)** of light nuclei **(1 mark)**
10.

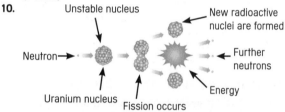

Unstable nucleus — New radioactive nuclei are formed — Neutron — Further neutrons — Uranium nucleus — Fission occurs — Energy

(7 correct = 4 marks; 5–6 correct = 3 marks; 3–4 correct = 2 marks; 1–2 correct = 1 mark)
11. **(a)** Nuclear reactor **(b)** Atomic bomb **(c) (i) and (ii)** Control rods; Moderator
12. Fission occurs in the nuclear reactor **(1 mark)**, this produces heat/thermal energy **(1 mark)**; this energy is used to heat water in the heat exchanger, which produces steam that then drives the turbines/makes the turbines rotate **(1 mark)**; the turbines are connected to the generator that turns to produce electricity **(1 mark)**
13. Cannot be predicted when radiation will be emitted/radiation is not emitted at constant intervals of time
14. **(a)** (Two) smaller nuclei **(1 mark)**, (More) neutrons **(1 mark)**, Energy **(1 mark) (b)** Radioactive **(c)** It must be stored/carefully disposed of
15. **(a)** Chain reaction **(b)** Neutron splits nucleus **(1 mark)**; (More) neutrons produced **(1 mark)**; Neutrons split more nuclei **(1 mark)**
16. Controlled: thermal energy used to make steam **(1 mark)** in nuclear reactor **(1 mark)**; Uncontrolled: enormous/huge amount of energy released **(1 mark)** in atomic bomb **(1 mark)**
17. Two or more light/small nuclei **(1 mark)** join/combine to form a heavy nuclei **(1 mark)** with the release of energy **(1 mark)**
18. **(a)** High temperature **(1 mark)** nuclei driven **(1 mark)** to overcome electrostatic repulsion **(1 mark)**
    (b) High pressure **(1 mark)** high density of nuclei **(1 mark)** ensures collisions **(1 mark)**
    (c) In stars
19.

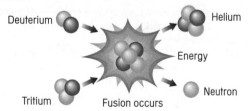

Deuterium — Helium — Energy — Tritium — Fusion occurs — Neutron

(6 correct = 3 marks; 4–5 correct = 2 marks; 2–3 correct = 1 mark)

20. **(a)** Temperature of fuel **(1 mark)** must be heated to 100 million °C/6 times hotter than the Sun **(1 mark)**
    (b) Pressure of fuel **(1 mark)** needs to be extremely high - this is difficult to achieve **(1 mark)**
    (c) Confinement of fuel **(1 mark)**, no ordinary vessel can be used (at such high temperatures and pressures) **(1 mark)**
*21. The theory of cold fusion is nuclear fusion which occurs at room temperature. However, fusion needs (very) high temperatures in order to take place because there is electrostatic repulsion between protons. As the experiment has not been reproduced convincingly by scientists, the theory of cold fusion is not generally accepted at the moment.

P2 Advantages and Disadvantages of Using Radioactive Materials (pages 66–70)

1. C **should be ticked.**
2. **(a)** Medical/food
   (b) Radon gas
3. **(a) and (b) Accept any two from:** Smoke alarm; Irradiating food; Sterilising equipment; Monitoring thickness; Diagnosis of cancer; Treatment of cancer; Dating of old fossils, etc.
4. **(a)** Time taken **(1 mark)** for half **(1 mark)** of the nuclei to change/decay **(1 mark)**
   (b) (i) 800Bq **(ii)** 200Bq **(c)** 3 p.m.
5. **(a)** 8 days
   *(b) Yes the scientists were right because the half-life of caesium is 30 years. So after four months it will still be very active and not much of it will have decayed. The half-life of iodine is much shorter than caesium at only 8 days (or the value quoted in (a)). After four months almost all or very nearly all of the iodine will have decayed.
6. **(a)** 2 original, one half-life 460 years; 3 original, two half-lives 920 years; $\frac{1}{8}$ original, three half-lives **(1 mark)** eight = 1380 years **(1 mark)**
   (b) Yes. Doesn't need replacing; still effective after a long time/many years
7. Can damage cells/cause cancer **(1 mark)**; Can cause mutations (in future generations) **(1 mark)**
8. **(a)** Alpha **(1 mark)** stopped **(1 mark)** by skin/can't penetrate body **(1 mark) (b)** Beta and gamma **(1 mark)** less likely to be absorbed by cells **(1 mark)**
9. **(a)** Protective clothing/not being too near **(b)** Limit exposure time/use short half-life source
10. **(a)** (Hands of) watches/aircraft instruments **(b)** Injuries/deaths reported
11. Advantages: **Accept any two from:** No air pollutants; Waste is small; Fuel costs low; Jobs created
    Disadvantages: **Accept any two from:** Risk of major accident; Waste dangerous; Transport/storage of waste difficult; Construction/maintenance costs high; Security a problem; A lot of land used; Visual pollution; Habitats destroyed; Increase in traffic causing noise/air pollution
12. **(a)** High level; medium level; low level **(b) (i)** Low level **(ii)** Protective clothing/laboratory equipment
13. **(a)** 50 years **(b)** One sixty-fourth $(\frac{1}{2})^6$
14. **(a)** Alpha absorbed by smoke but beta and gamma would not be **(1 mark)**; Alpha stopped by plastic case (so safe to use) **(1 mark)**
    (b) The alpha radiation ionises the air particles producing ions **(1 mark)**, which are attracted to the electrodes causing a current to flow **(1 mark)**; When there is a fire, alpha particles are absorbed by the smoke particles **(1 mark)**; This results in less ionisation and a smaller current to flow which activates the alarm/makes the alarm sound **(1 mark)**
15. **(a)** About 2 half-lives **(1 mark)** age about 2 × 5730 = 11460 years **(1 mark) (b) (i)** Because activity measured 450Bq not 435Bq **(ii)** Actual age should be (a bit) less
16. **(a)** Spent fuel rods **(1 mark)** short term: store in pool of liquid (to absorb radiation) **(1 mark)**; Long term: bury (deep) underground **(1 mark)** in (tightly) sealed containers **(1 mark)**
    (b) (i) Less radioactive **(ii)** Stored in drums/containers **(1 mark)** above ground **(1 mark)** and monitored **(1 mark)**

P3 Radiation in Treatment and Medicine (pages 71–78)

1. **Accept any one from:** CAT scans; X-rays; PET scans; MRI; Ionising radiation; Radioactivity; Light; Endoscope; Laser; Ultrasound
2. **(a)** False **(b)** True **(c)** True **(d)** False
3. Energy; Spreads out; Waves; Beta **(in that order)**
4. **(a)** Brightness less/dimmer **(b)** Reduces/decreases **(c)** Less (than before)
5. **(a)–(c)**

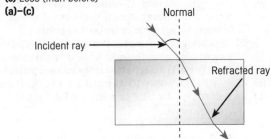

   (d) Greater than; towards **(e)** Speed decreases
6. **(a)**

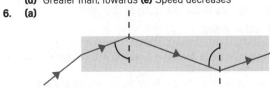

   (1 mark for a reflected beam at same angle as incident beam, 1 mark incident and reflected beams at bottom)
   (b) Total internal reflection
7. **(a)** Along edge of glass/boundary of air and glass
   (b)

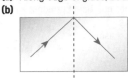

   (1 mark reflected ray drawn [at same angle])
   (c) 42°
8. **(a) (i) – (iii) Accept any three from:** Oesophagus; Stomach; Colon; Respiratory tract; Urinary tract; Reproductive system
   (b) No surgery
9. **(a)** Sound above 20000Hz/above limit of human hearing
   (b) (i) – (ii) Foetal scanning; Imaging kidneys/heart, etc.
   (c) Heats soft tissue **(1 mark)**; promotes/encourages blood flow **(1 mark)**
10. **(a)** Distance from focus **(1 mark)** to lens **(1 mark)**
    (b) Yes. Not real focus **(1 mark)**; focus in front of lens **(1 mark)**
11. **(a)**   **(b)**

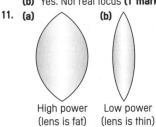

    High power   Low power
    (lens is fat)   (lens is thin)
    (1 mark for each correct diagram)
12. $\frac{1}{0.20}$ **(1 mark)** 5D **(1 mark)**
13.

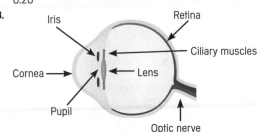

    (7 correct = 4 marks; 5–6 correct = 3 marks; 3–4 correct = 2 marks; 1–2 correct = 1 mark)

*14. He should hold the lens up to a light source, which is far away such as the light from a window (or something similar). He should project the image onto a screen or a piece of paper, which he holds behind the lens. He should then move the lens or the screen until the image is sharp. Lastly he needs to measure the distance from the lens to the screen. This distance is the focal length.

15. **(a) (i)** Not able to focus on/clearly see distant objects
    (ii) Caused by the eyeball being too long
    (b) Glasses/spectacles/contact lenses **(1 mark)** that are diverging **(1 mark)**

16.

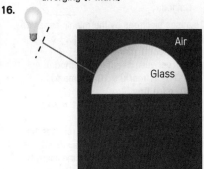

Dark paper

Direct a ray of light from a ray box, at the centre of a semi-circular glass block (placed on a sheet of dark paper). The light passes straight through from air to glass and the angle of refraction is always 90° to the surface. The critical angle can then be measured by marking the ray of light outside the block and the angle can be increased to find the critical angle.

17. **(a)** More dense = slower
    (b) Greater density, smaller critical angle
    (c) Slows down **(1 mark)** refracts **(1 mark)** towards the normal **(1 mark)**
18. **(a)** One bundle of (glass) fibres carries light to object **(1 mark)** other bundle returns reflected light **(1 mark)** to eyepiece **(1 mark)**
    (b) Devices can be attached **(1 mark)** to allow entry of medical instruments **(1 mark)**
19. **(a)** Light spread out over $4\pi 2^2$ **(1 mark)** $I = \frac{100}{4\pi 2^2}$ **(1 mark)** $= 2.0 Wm^{-2}$ **(1 mark)**
    (b) Area $= \frac{100}{0.5} = 200 m^2$ **(1 mark)** $4\pi r^2 = 200$ **(1 mark)**
    $r = \sqrt{(200/4\pi)} = 4.0m$ **(1 mark)** or I proportional to $\frac{1}{r^2}$ **(1 mark)** I reduced by 4 /is a quarter **(1 mark)** r doubled/increased by 2/4.0m **(1 mark)**
20. **(a)** $\frac{1}{0.1} + \frac{1}{0.2} = 10 + 5 = 15$ **(1 mark)**
    $f = \frac{1}{15} = \frac{0.067}{0.07m}$ **(1 mark)**
    (b) 15D
21. $\frac{1}{0.2} - \frac{1}{0.3}$ **(1 mark)** $= 1.67$ **(1 mark)** $v = \frac{1}{1.67} = 0.6m = 60cm$ **(1 mark)** real **(1 mark)**
22. **(a)** Within focal length/ u less than 10cm
    (b) (i) $\frac{1}{0.1} - \frac{1}{0.05} = -10$ **(1 mark)** $v = -0.1m = -10cm$ **(1 mark)**
    (ii) Virtual **(1 mark)** v or answer is negative **(1 mark)**
23. **(a)** $\frac{1}{0.5} + \frac{1}{(-0.2)}$ **(1 mark)** $= -3.0$ **(1 mark)** $\frac{1}{-3.0} = -0.33m$ **(1 mark)**
    (b) –3.0D
24. **(a)** Eyeball too short **(1 mark)** cornea/lens unable to refract light from near objects on to retina **(1 mark)** image on retina blurred/not sharp **(1 mark)**
    (b) Removes cornea tissue at edges **(1 mark)** curve of cornea increased **(1 mark)** increases power **(1 mark)**

P3 X-rays and ECGs (pages 79–84)

1. Metal; electrons; energy; escape; thermionic
2. (a)

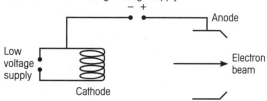

   (b) Heats up and releases electrons by thermionic emission
   (c) Reduces collisions with air particles **(1 mark)**; Collisions hinder electron movement **(1 mark)**
   (d) High voltage supply (between anode and cathode)
3. Current = Nq = 1000 × 0.01 **(1 mark)** = 10A **(1 mark)**
4. (a) True (b) False (c) True (d) True
5. Fluorescent screen **(1 mark)**; Made of crystals **(1 mark)**; Give off light when X-rays strike them **(1 mark)**;
*6. The X-rays spread out more so that less radiation reaches the image cassette. This is explained by the inverse square law. As the square of the distance from the source increases, the intensity decreases. So twice the distance means that a quarter of the X-rays or radiation will reach the cassette. This applies to all waves.
7. X-ray device **(1 mark)** that takes many pictures **(1 mark)** as source rotates **(1 mark)** computer processes information to build a cross-sectional image of the patient **(1 mark)**
8. X-rays are dangerous to an unborn child
9. Electrical discharge **(1 mark)** that travels through cell membrane **(1 mark)**
10. (a) Electrocardiogram
    (b) Electrical activity **(1 mark)** of heart **(1 mark)**
    (c) Gives information about the condition of the heart
11. (a) Heartbeat
    (b) Heartbeat is regular
    (c) T = 1.0s **(1 mark)** f = $\frac{1}{T}$ = 1.0s^{-1} **(1 mark)**
       Beats/min = f × 60 = 60 **(1 mark)**
12. (a) (Medical) device with electrodes **(1 mark)** contact heart muscles **(1 mark)**
    (b) (i) Blockage to electrical system (of heart)
        (ii) Heart can't beat fast enough
    (c) Delivers (electrical) impulses **(1 mark)** to heart to regulate beat **(1 mark)**
*13. (a) Pulse oximetry is a method to determine the amount of haemoglobin in a person's blood. A sensor is placed on a thin part of the body and two beams of light are sent through the body to the sensor. These beams are red and infrared of different wavelengths. A detector measures the intensity of light from each beam. The ratio of the amount of each wavelength that is absorbed determines the amount of oxygen in the blood.
    (b) (i)–(ii) **Accept any two from:** Intensive care; In surgery; In recovery
14. (a) (i) X-rays
        (ii) Cathode/filament
        (iii) Electron beam
        (iv) Anode
        (v) Target
    (b) (i) Copper/good conductor
        (ii) Conducts away heat **(1 mark)** produced in collision with target **(1 mark)**
15. (a) The thicker the material, the greater the absorption of the X-rays
    (b) Bones are thick or more dense so more X-rays are absorbed/soft tissue less thick or less dense so fewer X-rays are absorbed **(1 mark)**. The more X-rays are absorbed, the less they penetrate to X-ray image cassette **(1 mark)** and the less they darken the film/screen **(1 mark)**
16. (a) CAT scan: source + film/screen rotate and a cross-section view/slice through body seen **(1 mark)**; Normal X-ray scan: source + film stationary, and a flat image obtained **(1 mark)**
    (b) Computer processes/combines information **(1 mark)** from many images **(1 mark)**

17. (a) More/higher dose
    (b) X-ray taken to locate tumour **(1 mark)** several beams used to pinpoint (exact) location **(1 mark)**
18. (a) Time (s)
    (b) Potential difference (mV)
    (c) (i) P wave
        (ii) QRS wave
        (iii) T wave
    (d) (i) Depolarisation of atria **(1 mark)**; Electrical pulse causes contraction **(1 mark)**; Blood is forced into ventricles **(1 mark) Accept either of the last two points**
        (ii) Depolarisation of ventricles **(1 mark)**; Electrical pulse causes contraction **(1 mark)**; Blood is forced out of the heart **(1 mark) Accept either of the last two points**
19. (a) KE = 1.6 × 10^{-19} × 15 × 10^3 **(1 mark)** 2.4 × 10^{-15} J **(1 mark)**
    (b) 0.5 × m × v^2 = 2.4 × 10^{-15} **(or answer to (a), 1 mark)**
       $$v = \sqrt{\frac{(2.4 \times 10^{-15} \times 2)}{(9.1 \times 10^{-31})}}$$ **(1 mark)**
       = 72 627 304 m/s **(1 mark)** = 7.3 × 10^{7}m/s **(1 mark)**

P3 Production, Uses and Risks of Ionising Radiation from Radioactive Sources (pages 85–90)

1. D **should be ticked.**
2. Electrical charge; electrons; positive; negative; mass; opposite/positive **(6 correct = 3 marks; 4–5 correct = 2 marks; 2–3 correct = 1 mark)**
3. (a)–(e) Alpha; Beta; Gamma; Positron; Neutron **(In any order; 5 correct = 3 marks; 3–4 correct = 2 marks; 1–2 correct = 1 mark)**
4. (a) Gamma (b) Beta (c) Alpha (d) Neutron
   (e) Neutron/gamma
5. (a) A = mass number/number of neutrons + protons/number of nucleons; Z = atomic number/number of protons
   (b) (i) A the same; Z increases by 1
       (ii) A decreases by 4; Z decreases by 2
6. (a) Radioisotope **(1 mark)** used to trace /monitor **(1 mark)** part of the body **(1 mark)**
   (b) (i) Gamma
       (ii) Causes little ionisation/can easily be detected outside the body
7. (a) Positron emission tomography
   (b) (i) Affected
       (ii) Healthy
   (c) (i)–(ii) **Accept any two from:** Epilepsy; Multiple sclerosis; Schizophrenia; Alzheimer's; Disorders associated with drug/alcohol abuse
8. (a) Use of radioisotopes/radioactivity **(1 mark)** to destroy cancerous cells/tumours **(1 mark)**
   (b) **Accept one from:** Cobalt-60; Caesium-137; Iodine-131; Iridium-192; Californium-252
9. (a) False (b) True (c) False (d) True (e) True (f) True
10. (a) **Accept any two from:** Radiation can damage cells/tissue; Kill cells; Cause mutations
    (b) Limit exposure **(1 mark)** by reducing dose/performing task quickly/using protective clothing or screens/monitoring or using dosimeter **(1 mark)**
11. Medical care/treatment **(1 mark)** to lessen the severity of symptoms to improve quality of life **(1 mark)** and slow down progress of disease **(1 mark)**
*12. Isotopes used in PET scanners have short half-lives. Fluorine-18 has a half-life of 110 minutes or about 2 hours. The isotopes are used for more than one procedure or patient and each procedure on each patient can take many minutes. The activity of the isotope decreases significantly in a few hours and becomes less effective. If it is produced some distance away from the hospital, the travelling time reduces its effectiveness.
13. (a) Technetium-99m
    (b) (Technetium) absorbed by phosphate molecules **(1 mark)**; Bone cancer increases the production of phosphate **(1 mark)**; Technetium produces gamma rays which are seen as white shaded areas on PET scan **(1 mark)**
14. (a)–(b) **Accept any two from:** Hodgkin's disease; Non-Hodgkin's lymphoma; Oesophageal cancer; Head/neck cancer; Bowel cancer; Lung cancer; Prostate cancer

15. Iodine-131 **(1 mark)** taken orally **(1 mark)** treats overactive thyroid/thyroid cancer **(1 mark)**; Advantages: treats tumour directly/little effect on other parts of the body **(1 mark)**
16. **(a) Accept any two from:** Cause cancer; Tumours; DNA damage; Mutations
    (b) Accept any two from: Skin burns; Radiation sickness; Death
*17. PET scanning can identify cancers that other methods cannot, so it can help avoid unnecessary surgery. This saves money for the health service and reduces possible risks to the patient from surgery. At the same time, too many scans can increase the radiation dosage in a patient. Also, PET scanners are very expensive to buy and run, which could take money and resources away from other parts of the health service.
18. Nucleus **(1 mark)** has too many/too few neutrons **(1 mark)** compared to protons **(1 mark)** or ratio of n/p too high/low **(Accept either of the last two points)**
19. (a)–(c)

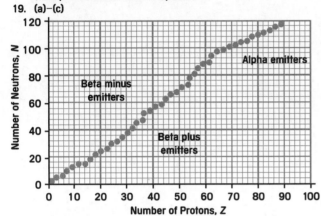

    (d) 1.0–1.2
    (e) 1.4–1.5
20. $$^{226}_{88}\text{Ra} \longrightarrow {}^{222}_{86}\text{Rn} + {}^{4}_{2}\alpha$$
    (Radium)   (Radon)   (Alpha particle)

    (1 mark for mass numbers 222 and 4 on the right-hand side 1 mark for atomic numbers 86 and 2 on the right-hand side)
21. **(a)** Made of quarks
    (b) (i) Up, up, down
        (ii) Up, down, down
22. **(a)** $+\frac{2}{3}$
    (b) $-\frac{1}{3}$
23. Neutron has 3 quarks **(1 mark)** up, down, down **(1 mark)** $+\frac{2}{3}, -\frac{1}{3}, -\frac{1}{3}$ (= zero) **(1 mark)**
24. Proton changes to neutron (+positron) **(1 mark)**; Proton has up, up, down; neutron has up, down, down **(1 mark)**; Up quark changes into a down quark **(1 mark)**
25. $\frac{1}{3}$ **(1 mark)** of proton/neutron mass **(1 mark)**

P3 Motion of Particles (pages 91–94)

1. C **should be ticked**.
2. B **should be ticked**.
3. **(a)–(b) Accept any two from:** Earth in orbit around the Sun; Point on spinning CD/DVD; Child on roundabout; Car going round a bend, etc.
4. Charged; Magnetic field; Circular; Speed; Particles **(5 correct = 3 marks; 3–4 correct = 2 marks; 1–2 correct = 1 mark)**
5. Elastic: momentum and KE same/conserved **(1 mark)** before and after collision **(1 mark)**; Inelastic: momentum same/conserved **(1 mark)** KE different after collision/not conserved **(1 mark)**
6. **(a)** Inelastic **(b)** 25 **(c)** 162.5 **(d)** 50 **(e)** Inelastic **(5 correct = 3 marks; 3–4 correct = 2 marks; 1–2 correct = 1 mark)**

7. **(a)** The isotopes produce gamma radiation **(1 mark)**; The isotope decays and emits a position, which is a positively charged electron **(1 mark)**; It collides with an electron and they annihilate each other **(1 mark)**; This produces energy in the form of gamma rays **(1 mark)**
   (b) (i)–(ii) Momentum and (kinetic) energy
   (c) Mass **(1 mark)** of positron and electron **(1 mark)** changed to energy **(1 mark)**
*8. Protons are accelerated by an electric field. This field is applied across the gaps of the D-shaped electrodes. A magnetic field forces the protons to move in circles or a spiral. The cyclotron is enclosed in a vacuum to eliminate collisions with air particles. (Exiting) protons bombard/strike a stable isotope. This changes the isotope by adding an extra proton to the nucleus.
9. **(a)** Negative electron = positive positron/or have equal and opposite charges **(1 mark)** so total charge before is zero **(1 mark)** gamma ray (photons) have no/zero charge **(1 mark)**
   (b) Electron mass = positron mass move at same speed in opposite directions **(1 mark)**; Momentum before is zero **(1 mark)**; Momentum after is zero since gamma rays have no mass **(1 mark)**
10. (Momentum before) $2250 \times 32 + 750 \times 22$ **(1 mark)** = 88 500 (kg m/s) **(1 mark)**
    (Momentum after) $3000 \times$ speed **(1 mark)** 29.5 m/s **(1 mark)**
11. **(a)** Before $0.17 \times 0.3 = 0.051$ (kg m/s) **(1 mark)**
        After $0.17 \times 0.029 + 0.15 \times v = 0.051$ **(1 mark)**
        $v = 0.31$ m/s **(1 mark)**
    (b) KE before $0.5 \times 0.17 \times 0.3^2 = 7.7 \times 10^{-3}$ (J) **(1 mark)**
        KE after $0.5 \times 0.17 \times 0.029^2 + 0.5 \times 0.15 \times 0.31^2 = 7.3 \times 10^{-3}$ (J) (7.14J if (a) = 0.307) **(1 mark)**
        Inelastic since KE before ≠ KE after **(1 mark)** They are nearly equal/might be elastic given that this is an experiment (and you get errors in experiments) **(1 mark)**
12. First (sphere) stops/speed is zero **(1 mark)**. Second (sphere) moves in same direction **(1 mark)** at 12cm/s or 0.12m/s **(1 mark)** to conserve momentum and KE (or could work these out to show they are equal before and after collision) **(1 mark)**

P3 Kinetic Theory and Gases (pages 95–98)

1. **(a)** Solid   **(b)** Liquid   **(c)** Gas
2. D **should be ticked.**
3. Moving; collide; force; pressure; greater; atmosphere **(6 correct = 3 marks; 4–5 correct = 2 marks; 2–3 correct = 1 mark)**
4. **(a)** −273°C   **(b)** No movement
5. **(a)** 273K   **(b)** 373 − 273 **(1 mark)** = 100°C **(1 mark)**
6. **(a)** Increase   **(b)** Increase by 2 times/doubles/twice
7. $\dfrac{800 \times 12\,000}{16\,000}$ **(1 mark)** = 600cm³ **(1 mark)**
*8.

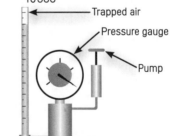

    (2 marks for labelled diagram)
    Connect a foot pump to a pressure gauge. This measures the pressure of air trapped by a column of oil in a vertical tube. Measure the length of the air column. We can assume that this is proportional to the volume of the air. Record the pressure and then increase the pressure by using the foot pump and take several readings of pressure and length (volume). Plot a graph of pressure against volume or one divided by the volume.
9. **(a)** Points plotted correctly (0,62), (50,75), (100,88) **(1 mark)**; straight line through −250°C **(1 mark)**
    (b) (i) −250°C **(ii)** Absolute zero **(iii)** −273°C
    (c) Accept any two from: Measurements wrong; Volumes should be more; Air may have leaked out

10. **(a)** Air is trapped in a capillary tube by a bead of (concentrated) sulfuric acid **(1 mark)**; The tube is placed in a water bath, the length of the air is proportional to the volume of the air if we assume that the cross-section of the tube is constant/uniform **(1 mark)**; The length of the air is measured at a number of different temperatures **(1 mark)**

  (b) We would expect to find that volume is proportional to temperature in Kelvin **(1 mark)**; A straight line should pass through -273K, though it may not do because of experimental errors **(1 mark)**

11. **(a)–(b) Accept any two from:** Relieve pain in labour/childbirth; Trauma; Oral surgery; Heart attacks

12. **(a)** (Much) more can be stored/transported **(1 mark)** in same space/volume **(1 mark)**

  (b) Regulates/adjusts pressure to deliver at atmospheric pressure **(1 mark)** at a suitable flow rate **(1 mark)**

13. $22°C = 295K$ **(1 mark)** $90 \times \dfrac{295}{80}$ **(1 mark)** $332K$ **(1 mark)** $59°C$ **(1 mark)**

14. Pressure $= \dfrac{600}{12} \times 1$ **(1 mark)** $= 50$ (atmospheres) **(1 mark)**

15. **(a)** $3500 \times 211 = V \times 101$ **(1 mark)** $V = 3500 \times \dfrac{211}{101} = 7312$ litres **(1 mark)**

  (b) $\dfrac{7312}{5} = 1462$ minutes **(1 mark)** $= 24.3$ hours $= 1$ day **(1 mark)**

11. The drawing below shows the main forces acting on a skydiver. (1)

Which statement correctly describes the situation that is shown?

A ⬭ Force P is weight and force Q is air resistance.

B ⬭ Force P is air resistance and force Q is acceleration.

C ⬭ Force P is acceleration and force Q is air resistance.

D ⬭ Force P is air resistance and force Q is weight.

12. The velocity–time graph below shows the motion of a skydiver at 10s intervals after he steps out of the aeroplane.

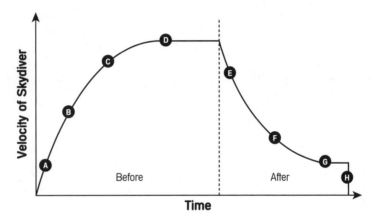

(a) Explain what happens at stages **A**, **B**, **C**, **and D**.

(i) A .... (1)

(ii) B .... (1)

(iii) C .... (1)

(iv) D .... (1)

(b) What stage does the dotted line represent? (1)

....

(c) Explain what happens at stages **E**, **F**, **G**, and **H**.

(i) E .... (1)

(ii) F .... (1)

(iii) G .... (1)

(iv) H .... (1)

*13. In an investigation into the relationship between force, mass and acceleration of a trolley, the runway being used should be raised up so that the trolley runs down a slope.
Explain why this is necessary. Discuss this statement. (6)

(Total: _____ / 49)

Higher Tier

14. A car travelling on a dual carriageway at constant velocity approaches a lorry just ahead. The car driver accelerates at $2m/s^2$ for 5 seconds to overtake the lorry. The car reaches 90km/hr. What was its velocity in m/s just before it accelerated? (4)

15. A passenger train accelerates out of a station at $0.8m/s^2$. If the driving force is 20 000N, work out the mass of the train. (1)

16. A car moves with constant speed of 30m/s. The combined mass of car plus driver is 1000kg.

(a) If the driving force is 3000N, what is the value of the resistive force? (1)

continued...

(b) If the driving force is increased to 4000N, calculate the acceleration of the car. (2)

....

(c) If the car accelerates for 20s at this acceleration. What will the velocity of the car be after this time? (2)

....

....

17. Look at the velocity–time graph, below, for a car's journey.

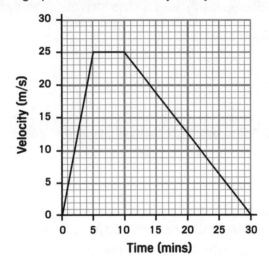

(a) What was the initial acceleration of the car? (2)

....

(b) What was the distance travelled at a constant velocity? (2)

....

(c) What was the total distance travelled? (2)

....

(d) What was the deceleration of the car on the final part of the journey? (2)

....

(e) What was the average velocity of the car for the whole journey? (2)

....

....

(Total: .... / 20)

P2 | Momentum, Energy, Work and Power

Questions labelled with an asterisk (*) are ones where the quality of your written communication will be assessed – you should take particular care with your spelling, punctuation and grammar, as well as the clarity of expression, on these questions.

1. The total stopping distance of a vehicle is the sum of **two** distances. What are they called? (2)

   (a) .... **(b)** ....

2. Which of the following conditions **will not** increase the stopping distance of a car? (1)

   A ☐ The car is travelling at high speed.   C ☐ The road is dry.

   B ☐ It is raining hard.   D ☐ The driver is sleepy.

3. A driver is driving steadily. She suddenly sees a child step out in front of her car. She brakes.

   (a) What is meant by the driver's 'reaction time'? (2)

   ....

   ....

   (b) Apart from feeling tired, name **two** other things that could increase reaction time.

   (i) .... (1)

   (ii) .... (1)

4. A woman is learning to drive. Her driving instructor points out the various features of the car. Below is a list of features. Which one is a safety feature? (1)

   A ☐ Sat-nav   C ☐ Metallic paint

   B ☐ Air bag   D ☐ Alloy wheels

5. What **two** things do you need to know to calculate the momentum of a vehicle? (2)

   (a) .... **(b)** ....

6. A car of mass 1000kg travels at a constant velocity of 20m/s.

   (a) Calculate the momentum of the car. (2)

   ....

   (b) Another car of the same mass is travelling at the same velocity but in the **opposite** direction. What is the momentum of this car? (1)

   ....

7. Use the equation **velocity** $= \dfrac{\text{momentum}}{\text{mass}}$ to calculate the velocity of a motorbike if its mass is 250kg, the rider has a mass of 90kg and its momentum is 8500kg m/s. (3)

   ....

   ....

8. In a collision between two bodies, momentum is **conserved**.

    (a) What does this mean?   (1)

_____

    (b) Two cars are travelling in the same direction. They both have the same mass of 800kg. The velocity of the one in front is 20m/s. The other is moving at 30m/s.

    At some point, the cars will collide.

       (i) Calculate the total momentum before they collide.   (2)

_____

_____

       (ii) Write down the total momentum after they collide.   (1)

_____

9. A cyclist moves along a level road against resistive forces of 150N. He travels 1500m. Calculate the work done by the cyclist.   (2)

_____

10. A man lifts up a parcel of weight 50N from the ground through a distance of 1.8m.   (2)

    (a) How much work does he do?

_____

    (b) How much energy does he transfer?   (1)

_____

    (c) Explain your answer to **(b)**.   (1)

_____

11. A crane on a building site lifts a load of 50 000N through a distance of 30m.

    (a) Calculate the work done.   (2)

_____

    (b) If this takes 20s, calculate the power output of the crane.   (2)

_____

12. **(a)** What is **gravitational potential energy** (GPE)? (1)

....

....

(b) Give **two** examples of objects that have GPE.

(i) .... (1)

(ii) .... (1)

13. A girl climbs 5m up a tree. Her mass is 50kg. Work out her gravitational potential energy. (2)

....

14. A football of mass 0.4kg is kicked into the air to a height of 8m.

(a) Calculate the gravitational potential energy that the ball gains. (2)

....

(b) What happens to this energy as the ball starts to fall back to the ground? (1)

....

15. Give **two** examples of objects that have kinetic energy.

(a) .... (1)

(b) .... (1)

16. A lorry of mass 2000kg moves at 20m/s. Calculate the kinetic energy of the lorry. (2)

....

....

17. Energy can only be transferred from one form to another. Draw a line to match each example to the correct description of how energy is transferred. (4)

(a) Using an iron	**(i)** Potential energy to kinetic energy to potential energy
(b) Speaking into a mobile phone	
	(ii) Kinetic energy to heat (thermal) energy
(c) A child on a park swing	
	(iii) Sound energy to electrical energy
(d) A car stopping at traffic lights	
	(iv) Electrical energy to heat (thermal) energy

*18. Outline an experiment you could perform in a school laboratory to investigate how the force needed to move a wooden block depends on the type of surface. (6)

_____

_____

_____

_____

_____

_____

_____

_____

_____

19. In terms of momentum change, explain how the air bags in a car protect the passengers. (3)

_____

_____

_____

20. The velocity-time graph below shows a car having to make an emergency stop.

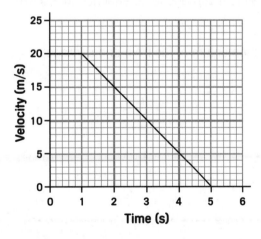

Use the graph to answer the following questions.

(a) How fast was the car travelling before it braked? _____ (1)

(b) What was the thinking distance? _____ (1)

(c) How long did it take the car to come to rest after the brakes were applied? (1)

_____

(d) What was the overall stopping distance? _____ (1)

21. In a hydro-electric plant, 10^4 kg of water is pumped back up to the upper reservoir through a distance of 120m.

(a) Calculate the work done by the pumps. (2)

_____

(b) This process takes 3 minutes 20 seconds. Calculate the power output of the pumps. (2)

_____

22. Which of the following statements best describes the principle of the conservation of energy? Tick the correct statement. (1)

A ◯ Energy is constantly being lost, so new energy needs to be generated.

B ◯ New energy is constantly being formed, so the total amount of energy grows.

C ◯ Energy cannot be made, lost or transferred.

D ◯ It is only possible to transfer energy to different forms.

(Total: _____ / 64)

Higher Tier

23. A train engine reverses on to a carriage to be attached to it. It exerts a force of 2000N over a period of 0.45s.

Calculate the change in momentum of the train and carriage. (4)

_____

_____

_____

_____

continued...

24. A car of mass 750kg is travelling at 20m/s. It is forced to slow suddenly to a velocity of 5m/s in a time of 5s.

(a) Calculate the change in momentum. (2)

(b) Now calculate the force exerted on the driver. (2)

25. (a) What is the relationship between a car's kinetic energy and the work done to stop it? (1)

(b) Hence show that the stopping distance of a car is proportional to the square of its velocity. (4)

(c) A lorry of mass 5000kg travelling at 25m/s brakes by applying a force of 10 000N. What is its stopping distance? (2)

*26. Habiba and Connor are talking about the stopping distance of a vehicle. Connor thinks that the stopping distance is directly proportional to speed because it takes more energy to stop it if it is moving faster. Habiba disagrees. She says that the stopping distance is much more at greater speeds, so it cannot be proportional to speed.

Who is right? Explain the physics behind your answer. (6)

(Total: .... / 21)

Questions labelled with an asterisk (*) are ones where the quality of your written communication will be assessed – you should take particular care with your spelling, punctuation and grammar, as well as the clarity of expression, on these questions.

1. The diagram below shows a simple model of a lithium (Li) atom. Lithium has an atomic number of 3 and a mass number of 7.

    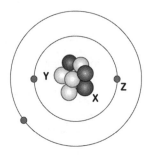

    Name the particles **X**, **Y** and **Z**.

    (a) X = ...   **(b) Y =** ....   (3)

    (c) Z = ...

2. The atomic number of cobalt is 27. Cobalt has two isotopes, cobalt-60 and cobalt-59.

    (a) What is an isotope?   (2)

    ....

    ....

    (b) Fill in the missing information about the two isotopes of cobalt to complete the table below.   (3)

	Cobalt-60	Cobalt-59
(i) Number of protons		
(ii) Number of neutrons		
(iii) Number of electrons		

3. The various isotopes of an element, X, are written in the following way: $^{A}_{Z}X$

    What do the letters *A* and *Z* represent?   (2)

    A = ...

    Z = ...

4. Lithium can be represented as $^{7}_{3}Li$

    Represent cobalt-60 and cobalt-59 in the same way.   (2)

    Cobalt-60 ....   Cobalt-59 ....

5. What do we mean if we say that a substance is **radioactive**? (1)

6. Draw lines to link each different type of radiation to the relevant description/s. A description can apply to more than one type of radiation. (3)

(i) Emitted from a nucleus

(ii) Very high-frequency radiation

(a) Alpha

(iii) Consists of two protons and two neutrons

(b) Beta

(iv) Very short wavelength radiation

(c) Gamma

(v) Fast-moving electron

(vi) Has a negative charge

(vii) A helium nucleus

7. Alpha, beta and gamma radiation are directed at three absorbers, as shown below.

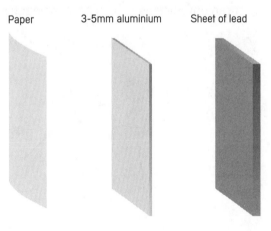

Paper   3-5mm aluminium   Sheet of lead

(a) Which radiation or radiations will still be detected after going through the sheet of paper? (1)

(b) Which absorbers will not let beta radiation through them? (1)

(c) Which radiation or radiations will still be detected after passing through the lead? (1)

8. Alpha, beta and gamma radiation are all said to be ionising radiations.

(a) What is the meaning of **ionise** or **ionising**? (3)

....

....

(b) These radiations have different ionising powers. Which radiation has the strongest ionising

power? .... (1)

9. Nuclear fission and nuclear fusion are processes that release large amounts of energy.
What is the difference between them? (4)

Nuclear fission ....

....

Nuclear fusion ....

....

10. The diagram below shows part of a nuclear fission process. Write the following labels in the
correct places on the diagram. (4)

energy   **neutron**   **unstable nucleus**   **fission occurs**

further neutrons   **uranium nucleus**   **new radioactive nuclei are formed**

11. Chain reactions can be **controlled** or **uncontrolled**. Give an example of:

(a) a controlled chain reaction .... (1)

(b) an uncontrolled chain reaction. .... (1)

(c) Name the **two** methods of controlling a chain reaction.

(i) .... (1)

(ii) .... (1)

12. Below is a diagram of a type of nuclear reactor.

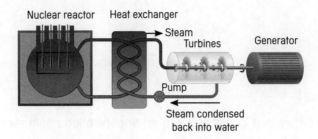

Explain how electricity is produced from a nuclear reactor. (4)

_____

_____

_____

_____

_____

_____

_____

13. An unstable nucleus emits radiation at **random**. What do you understand by this? (1)

_____

14. **(a)** What are the products of nuclear fission? (3)

_____

_____

(b) Are these products radioactive or non-radioactive? (1)

_____

(c) What potential problem does this pose? (1)

_____

_____

15. Once nuclear fission has started, it continues by itself.

(a) What is the term used to describe a self-sustaining reaction like this? (1)

_____

(b) Describe how this reaction continues. (3)

16. What is the difference between a **controlled** and an **uncontrolled** chain reaction? (4)

Controlled

Uncontrolled

17. Explain what happens during the nuclear fusion process. (3)

18. Name and explain **two** conditions that must be met before nuclear fusion can occur.

(a) (3)

(b) (3)

(c) Where in the Universe are these conditions met?

(1)

19. Using the words below, label the diagram appropriately to show a nuclear fusion reaction. (3)

deuterium   helium   tritium   energy   neutron   fusion occurs

....

....

....

....

(Total: .... / 66)

20. Explain the **three** practical problems involved in producing energy from nuclear fusion.

(a) .... (2)

....

(b) .... (2)

....

(c) .... (2)

....

*21. Explain the theory of **cold fusion**. Why is this not an accepted theory? (6)

....

....

....

....

....

....

....

....

....

....

(Total: .... / 12)

P2 Advantages and Disadvantages of Using Radioactive Materials

Questions labelled with an asterisk (*) are ones where the quality of your written communication will be assessed – you should take particular care with your spelling, punctuation and grammar, as well as the clarity of expression, on these questions.

1. What is meant by **background radiation**? (1)

    A ◯ Radiation that is produced by someone working in the background.

    B ◯ Radiation that occurs from the fall-out of atomic bombs.

    C ◯ Radiation that occurs in the environment.

    D ◯ Radiation that occurs from outer space.

2. The following are some of the sources of background radiation.

    radon gas   **nuclear industry**   **cosmic rays**   **gamma rays**

    (a) Name **one** other source. (1)

    (b) Which one of the above sources contributes most to background radiation? (1)

3. Name **two** uses of radioactivity.

    (a) .... (1)

    (b) .... (1)

4. **(a)** What is meant by the half-life of a radioactive source? (3)

    (b) A radioactive source has a half-life of 1 hour. Its activity is measured as 1600Bq at 9 a.m. What would its activity be at:

    (i) 10 a.m.? (1)

    (ii) 12 p.m.? (1)

    (c) At what time would its activity be 25Bq? (1)

5. The explosion at the Chernobyl Nuclear Reactor released a large cloud of radioactive gas into the atmosphere that spread over Europe. The gas contained caesium-137 (with a half-life of 30 years) and iodine-131. The following table shows measurements of the count rate, in bequerels, from a small amount of iodine-131.

Time (days)	0	4	8	12
Count Rate (Bq)	320	250	160	125

(a) From the table above, work out the half-life of iodine-131. (1)

*(b) Four months after the explosion, scientists were no longer concerned about the health risks from the iodine but were still worried about the effects of the caesium-137. Do you think that they were right to be concerned about the caesium but not about the iodine? Explain your answer. (6)

6. (a) Americium-241 is used in smoke detectors. It has a half-life of 460 years. How long will it take for the number of radioactive atoms in a sample of Americium-241 to decrease to $\frac{1}{8}$ of the original number? (2)

(b) Do you think that it is a good idea to use a radioactive isotope with such a long half-life? Explain your answer. (1)

7. Why is ionising radiation dangerous to humans? (2)

8. The damaging effects of radiation depend on whether the radiation source is outside or inside the body.

(a) Which type/s of ionising radiation is not harmful to the inside of the body when the source is outside? Explain your answer. (2)

(b) Which types of ionising radiation are less harmful when the source is inside the body? Explain your answer. (2)

....

....

9. A nurse is delivering radiotherapy to a patient. What type of precautions should she take:

(a) for her own protection? (1)

....

....

(b) for her patient's protection? (1)

....

....

10. In 1901, radium was first used to treat patients with cancerous tumours.

(a) Radium-based paint was invented a few years later. What was it used for? (1)

....

(b) Why were substances containing radium removed from use in the 1930s? (1)

....

11. State **two** advantages and **two** disadvantages of using nuclear power to generate electricity.

Advantages: (2)

....

....

Disadvantages: (2)

....

....

12. There are **three** different types of nuclear waste.

(a) What are they? (1)

....

(b) (i) Which one is the most common type that has to be dealt with? (1)

....

(ii) Where does this waste come from? (2)

_____

_____

13. The graph below shows the decay of a radioactive isotope.

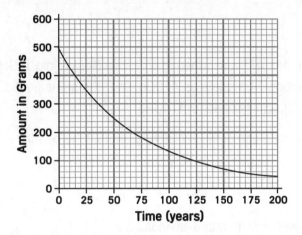

(a) What is the average half-life of this material? (1)

_____

(b) What fraction of the material would remain after 300 years? (1)

_____

14. A smoke alarm makes use of a radioactive isotope. The diagram below shows a simple smoke detector.

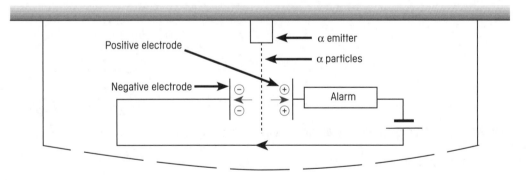

(a) Give **two** reasons why a source emitting alpha particles, rather than beta or gamma rays, is used. (2)

_____

_____

_____

(b) Explain how the smoke alarm works. (4)

15. Part of the skeleton of an animal is unearthed in an archaeological dig. A Geiger counter measures the activity of radioactive carbon-14 present as 450Bq. Over the same period of time, the same mass of new bone has an average activity of about 1740Bq.

(a) Calculate the approximate age of the skeleton, given that the half-life of carbon-14 is 5730 years. (2)

(b) (i) Why is your answer only an approximation? (1)

(ii) Should the actual age be more or less than the answer you gave in **(a)**? (1)

16. One disadvantage of using nuclear power for electricity generation is the waste produced.

(a) Where does high-level waste come from and what can be done about it in the short and long term? (4)

(b) Other waste accounts for nearly all of the waste produced.

(i) Why is it not as dangerous as high-level waste? (1)

(ii) What is done with this kind of waste? (3)

(Total: .... / 59)

Radiation in Treatment and Medicine | P3

Questions labelled with an asterisk (*) are ones where the quality of your written communication will be assessed – you should take particular care with your spelling, punctuation and grammar, as well as the clarity of expression, on these questions.

1.   Name **one** way in which medical physicists use radiation to help doctors in diagnosis or treatment.   (1)

2.   Write **true** or **false** next to the following statements about the uses of radiation in medicine.

   (a) A CAT scanner is a machine to look at cats. ....   (1)

   (b) The endoscope uses light to look inside the body. ....   (1)

   (c) Ultrasound can help diagnose problems with the foetus. ....   (1)

   (d) Lasers use ionising radiation to treat skin problems. ....   (1)

3.   Use words from the following list to complete the paragraph below.   (4)

   waves   **spreads out**   **energy**   **beta**

   The word radiation can describe any kind of .... that ....

   from a source. It can to refer light or sound .... or to particles such as alpha or

   .... radiation.

4.   Francine switches on her torch to carry out some experiments.

   (a) If she moves away from the light, she notices that the brightness changes. How does it change?   (1)

   (b) How does the **intensity** of the light change?   (1)

   (c) Her torch is waterproof. She puts it into a glass beaker of water and moves the same distance away from the light as before. What does she now notice about the intensity of the light?   (1)

5. A ray of light is directed at a glass block from a ray-box. The path of the ray is drawn before it enters the block and after it leaves the block.

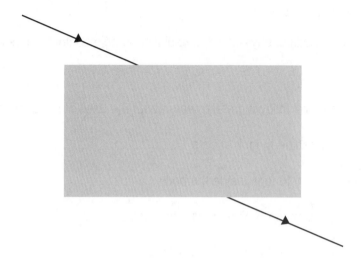

Complete the ray diagram to show:

(a) the path of the light ray through the glass block (1)

(b) the normal as the incident ray enters the block. (1)

The angle of incidence is the angle between the incident ray and the normal. The angle of refraction is the angle between the refracted ray and the normal.

(c) Label the incident ray and the refracted ray. (2)

(d) Underline or ⟨circle⟩ the correct word or words in the following: (2)

When light passes from air to glass, the angle of incidence is **less than / greater than** the angle of refraction. Light bends **towards / away from** the normal.

(e) What happens to the speed of the light as it passes through the glass? (1)

6. The following diagram shows a light beam within a glass fibre. Its angle of incidence is greater than the critical angle.

Glass fibre

(a) Complete the ray diagram to show what happens to the beam as it travels down the fibre. (2)

(b) What is this called? (1)

7. The following diagram shows a ray for which the angle of incidence is the critical angle of 42° for the glass.

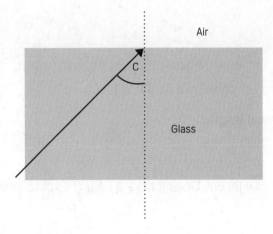

(a) The angle of refraction is 90°. Where does the ray refract? (1)

_____

As well as refraction, a weaker reflection occurs.

(b) Draw the reflected ray. (1)

(c) What is the size of the angle of reflection? _____ (1)

8. Optical fibres are used in medical endoscopes.

(a) Suggest **three** parts of the body that endoscopes can be used to examine.

(i) _____ (1)

(ii) _____ (1)

(iii) _____ (1)

(b) The procedure is **non-invasive**. What does this mean? (1)

_____

9. **(a)** What is meant by **ultrasound**? (1)

_____

(b) State **two** uses of ultrasound in diagnosis.

(i) _____ (1)

(ii) _____ (1)

(c) Ultrasound can be used for treatment of wounds to speed up healing. How is it thought that it does this? (2)

....

....

10. **(a)** A converging lens brings or converges light to a focus.

What is meant by its **focal length**? (2)

....

(b) A diverging lens spreads light out. Does it have a focus? Explain your answer. (2)

....

....

11. The **power** of a lens is related to its shape. In the space below, draw a converging lens with

(a) High power   **(b)** Low power (2)

12. The focal length of a converging lens is 0.20m. What is its power? (2)

....

....

13. Here is a diagram of the eye.

Label the diagram to show the **cornea**, the **iris**, the **pupil**, the **lens**, the **retina**, the **optic nerve** and the **ciliary muscles**. (4)

*14. Ryan is given a converging lens and told to find its focal length.

Describe how he should do this. (6)

15. **(a) (i)** What is **short sight**? (1)

(ii) How is it caused? (1)

(b) How can short sight be corrected? (2)

*16. Describe how you could, in the school laboratory, measure the critical angle for light travelling from glass into air. You may include a labelled diagram in your answer if this helps. (6)

17. **(a)** How does the speed of light depend on the density of a material that light passes through? (1)

(b) Below is a table showing the densities of different materials, together with their critical angles with air.

Material	Critical Angle with Air (°)	Density (kg/m³)
Ice	50	920
Water	49	1000
Perspex	42	1190
Crown glass	41	2600
Diamond	24	3300

What is the relationship between the density of a material and its critical angle with air? (1)

....

(c) What would happen if light travels at an angle from water into Perspex? (3)

....

....

18. The diagram below shows a medical endoscope.

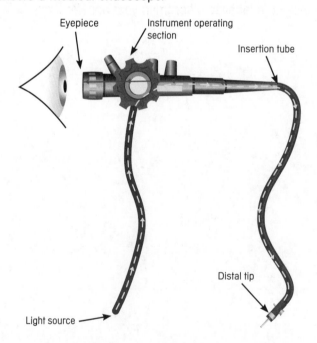

Eyepiece

Instrument operating section

Insertion tube

Distal tip

Light source

(a) Describe briefly how a medical endoscope works. (3)

....

....

....

(b) What is the purpose of the distal tip? (2)

_____

_____

(Total: _____ / 72)

Higher Tier

19. The power of a light bulb is 100W.

    (a) Calculate its intensity at a distance of 2.0m. (3)

_____

_____

    (b) At what distance will its intensity decrease to $0.5W/m^2$? (3)

_____

_____

20. An object is placed 0.1m from a converging lens. A real image is produced 0.2m from the lens.

    (a) What is its focal length? (2)

_____

_____

    (b) State its power. _____ (1)

21. An object is placed 30cm from a converging lens of focal length 20cm. Calculate the position of the image formed. Is the image real or virtual? (4)

_____

_____

_____

22. A converging lens has a focal length of 10cm.

    (a) Where should an object be placed to obtain a magnified image? (1)

_____

continued...

(b) (i) Calculate the position of the image when the object distance is 5cm. (2)

(ii) Is the image real or virtual? How can you tell from your answer? (2)

23. An object is placed 0.5m from a diverging lens. A virtual image is formed 0.2m from the lens.

(a) Calculate the focal length of the lens. (3)

(b) What is its power? (1)

24. **(a)** Explain, fully, in terms of the image on the retina, what is meant by **long sight**. (3)

(b) How would laser surgery be able to correct this? (3)

(Total: _____ / 28)

Questions labelled with an asterisk (*) are ones where the quality of your written communication will be assessed – you should take particular care with your spelling, punctuation and grammar, as well as the clarity of expression, on these questions.

1. Use the following words to complete the passage below. (5)

energy　　**thermionic**　　**metal**　　**escape**　　**electrons**

When a _____ is heated, some of the _____ gain enough

_____ to _____. This is known as

_____ emission.

2. The diagram below shows part of an electron gun.

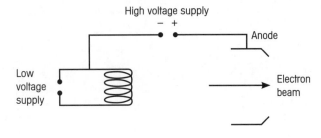

High voltage supply
− +
Anode

Low voltage supply

Electron beam

(a) Label the cathode on the diagram. (1)

(b) What does the filament do? (1)

_____

(c) Why is the device enclosed in a vacuum? (2)

_____

(d) What makes the electrons accelerate towards the anode? (1)

_____

3. 1000 particles, each with a charge of 0.01C, pass through a point in an electric circuit in 1 second. Calculate the current that flows. (2)

_____

4. Write **true** or **false** next to each of the following statements about using X-rays in hospitals.

(a) X-ray machines can take internal pictures of a patient. _____ (1)

(b) X-rays are not dangerous to use. _____ (1)

(c) X-rays leave an image on a photographic film or screen. _____ (1)

(d) On a normal X-ray image, bones appear white. _____ (1)

5. A fluoroscope is an X-ray device. It allows the viewing of live images. How is this possible? (3)

....

....

*6. A screen is positioned 1.5m from an X-ray tube and an image is taken of a patient's chest. The X-ray tube is then moved away so that it is now 3m from the screen. The image seen does not look the same. Explain why. Does this only apply to X-rays? (6)

....

....

....

....

....

....

....

....

....

7. What is a CAT scan? (4)

....

....

....

8. Why is ultrasound preferred to the use of X-rays to examine an unborn child? (1)

....

9. What is an **action potential**? (2)

....

....

10. (a) What do the letters **ECG** stand for? (1)

....

(b) What does an ECG measure? (2)

_____

_____

(c) What information does an ECG provide to the doctor? (1)

_____

11. A typical ECG from a healthy person is shown below.

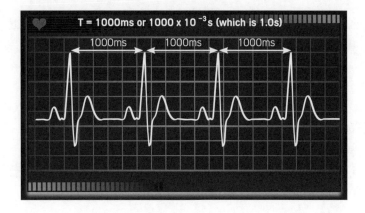

(a) What does the time between the peaks allow the doctor to measure? (1)

_____

(b) The time is constant. What can this information tell the doctor about the condition of the heart? (1)

_____

(c) Calculate the heart rate in beats/minute. (3)

_____

_____

12. (a) What is a **pacemaker**? (2)

_____

(b) Why might a pacemaker be necessary? Give **two** reasons.

(i) _____ (1)

(ii) _____ (1)

(c) What does a pacemaker do to treat these problems? (2)

_____

_____

*13. (a) Explain what is meant by **pulse oximetry**. (6)

(b) Give **two** situations in which pulse oximetry is needed.

(i) .... (1)

(ii) .... (1)

14. The diagram below shows the cross-section of an X-ray machine.

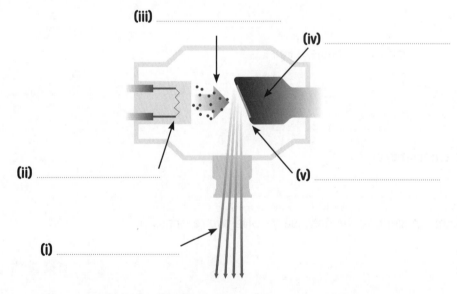

(iii) ....

(iv) ....

(ii) ....

(v) ....

(i) ....

(a) Label the diagram by adding appropriate words in the spaces (i)–(v). (5)

(b) (i) What is the anode usually made of? .... (1)

(ii) What is the function of the anode? (2)

....

15. **(a)** What is the relationship between the absorption of X-rays and the thickness of the material through which they travel? (1)

(b) Why do bones appear white and soft tissue appear black on an X-ray? (3)

16. **(a)** What are the essential differences between a CAT scan and a normal X-ray scan? (2)

(b) How is a 3-dimensional image obtained? (2)

17. **(a)** How does the amount of radiation delivered during a CAT scan compare to that from a normal X-ray procedure? (1)

(b) High-energy gamma rays are often used to treat cancerous tumours. Lower-energy X-rays are also used, however. Explain their role. (2)

18. The trace below shows a single cardiac cycle, taken from an ECG trace.

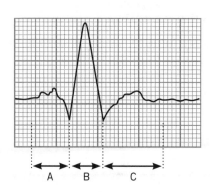

(a) What is recorded along the horizontal-axis of the trace? Give the units. (1)

(b) What is recorded along the vertical-axis of the trace? Give the units. (1)

....

(c) Give the names of the **three** waveforms that are marked on the graph. (3)

   (i) A ....

   (ii) B ....

   (iii) C ....

(d) State and explain the actions that give rise to waveforms **A** and **B**.

   (i) A .... (2)

   ....

   (ii) B .... (2)

   ....

(Total: .... **/ 83)**

Higher Tier

19. A potential difference of 15kV is applied between the anode and cathode of an X-ray machine.

   (a) Calculate the energy gained by an electron accelerated through this p.d.
      (The charge on an electron is 1.6×10^{-19}C.) (2)

   ....

   (b) If the mass of an electron is 9.1×10^{-31}kg, calculate the velocity gained by the electron.
      Give your answer in standard form, to two significant figures. (4)

   ....

   ....

(Total: .... **/ 6)**

Questions labelled with an asterisk (*) are ones where the quality of your written communication will be assessed – you should take particular care with your spelling, punctuation and grammar, as well as the clarity of expression, on these questions.

1. If a proton has a mass of 1 unit, what is the approximate mass of an electron? Tick the correct answer. (1)

    A ◯ 1 unit   B ◯ −1 unit

    C ◯ $\frac{1}{200}$ unit   D ◯ $\frac{1}{2000}$ unit

2. Use the words below to complete the following information about atoms. (3)

    positive   **opposite**   **electrons**   **mass**   **electrical charge**   **negative**

    Overall, an atom does not have an .... This is because the number of protons is

    equal to the number of .... A proton has a .... charge. An

    electron has a .... charge. A positron has the same ....

    as an electron but .... charge.

3. Name the **five** types of radioactive radiation. (3)

    (a) ....   **(b)** ....   **(c)** ....

    (d) ....   **(e)** ....

4. Which radiation:

    (a) is not a particle? .... (1)

    (b) has a negative charge? .... (1)

    (c) is the most ionising? .... (1)

    (d) is a particle carrying no electrical charge? .... (1)

    (e) is unaffected by an electric field? .... (1)

5. The various isotopes of an element, X, are distinguished by using the notation $^{A}_{Z}X$

    (a) What do the letters **A** and **Z** represent? (2)

    A = ...

    Z = ...

    (b) What happens to **A** and **Z** in:

    (i) negative beta decay? (2)

    ....

(ii) alpha decay? (2)

6. **(a)** What is a radioactive tracer, used in medicine? (3)

(b) Tracing the blood stream through an organ is an example of its use in medical diagnosis.

    (i) What radiation is used? (1)

    (ii) Explain why this radiation is used. (1)

7. **(a)** What do the letters PET stand for in **PET scanner**? (1)

(b) The images below show the brain of a healthy person and the brain of a person suffering from Parkinson's disease.

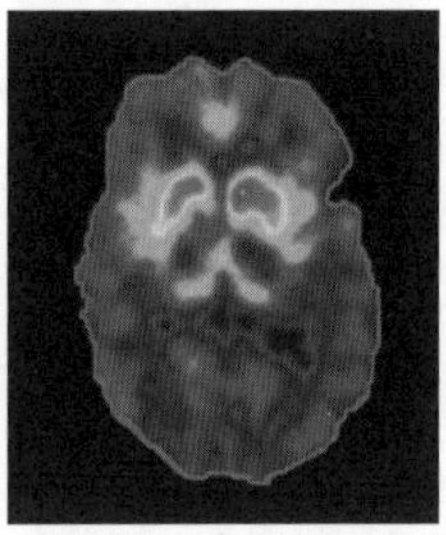

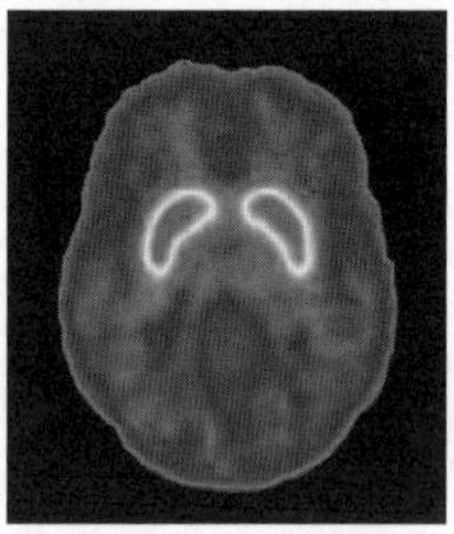

    (i) _____   **(ii)** _____

Label the images to show which is the healthy brain and which is the affected brain. (1)

(c) Name **two** other conditions that affect the brain that can be detected through PET scanning. (2)

    (i)

    (ii)

8. **(a)** What is radiotherapy? (2)

(b) Give **one** example of the type of source used in radiotherapy. (1)

9. Write **true** or **false** next to each of the following statements about radiotherapy.

    (a) Multiple beam therapy causes excessive damage to healthy tissue. .... (1)

    (b) Multiple beam therapy is used for deeply embedded tumours. .... (1)

    (c) Radiotherapy treatment consists of a single dose. .... (1)

    (d) Radiation can be given internally. .... (1)

    (e) Radiation can be given externally. .... (1)

    (f) Internal radiotherapy is used only in specialised cases. .... (1)

10. **(a)** Why is it important to protect people from ionising radiation? (2)

    (b) Describe **one** way in which people can be protected. (2)

11. What is meant by **palliative care**? (3)

*12. The radioisotopes used in PET scanners need to be produced within or near to the hospital. Explain why. (6)

Production, Uses and Risks of Ionising Radiation from Radioactive Sources

13. **(a)** What radioisotope is used to detect bone cancers? (1)

(b) How is bone cancer detected by using this radioisotope in a PET scan? (3)

14. PET scans are also used to diagnose other cancers. Name **two** examples.

(a) .... **(b)** .... (2)

15. Describe a use of internal radiotherapy. State **one** advantage that this has. (4)

16. What are the dangers of:

(a) being exposed to low doses of radiation over a prolonged period of time? (2)

(b) high doses of ionising radiation? (2)

***17.** What are the social and ethical issues related to the use of PET scanning in hospitals? (6)

(Total: .... / 69)

18. What affects the stability of the atom? (2)

....

....

19. The graph below shows the number of neutrons, **N** plotted against the number of protons, **Z** for stable isotopes.

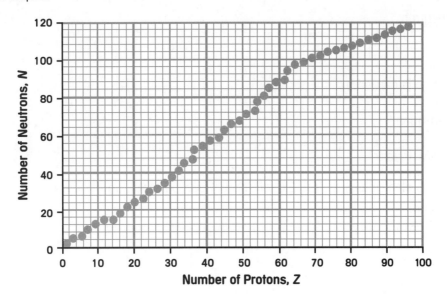

Mark on the diagram the regions where you would expect to find:

(a) unstable isotopes that emit beta minus particles (1)

(b) unstable isotopes that emit beta plus particles (1)

(c) unstable isotopes that emit alpha particles. (1)

What is the ratio of $\dfrac{N}{Z}$ if **Z** is:

(d) less than 20? .... (1)

(e) more than 50? .... (1)

20. Radium decays into radon with the emission of an alpha particle. Complete the nuclear equation below by writing in the mass and atomic numbers for radon and an alpha particle. (2)

$$^{226}_{88}\text{Ra} \longrightarrow \text{Rn} + \alpha$$

(Radium)   (Radon)   (Alpha particle)

continued...

21. Protons and neutrons are not fundamental particles.

(a) Why not? (1)

....

(b) Describe the arrangement of the main fundamental particles that make up a:

(i) proton (1)

....

(ii) neutron. (1)

....

22. What charge is carried by:

(a) the up-quark? .... (1)

(b) the down-quark? .... (1)

23. A neutron is electrically neutral. Explain how it can be made up of quarks that carry charge. (3)

....

....

....

....

24. How do you explain beta plus decay in terms of quarks? (3)

....

....

....

....

25. The mass of a proton is about the same as that of a neutron. What is the effective mass

of a quark? .... (2)

(Total: .... / 22)

Questions labelled with an asterisk (*) are ones where the quality of your written communication will be assessed – you should take particular care with your spelling, punctuation and grammar, as well as the clarity of expression, on these questions.

1. A stone is tied to a piece of string and is swung in a circle. What is the name of the force acting on the stone? (1)

   A ◯ Centrifugal force

   B ◯ Resultant force

   C ◯ Centripetal force

   D ◯ Tension force

2. The stone in question 1 is constantly accelerating towards the centre of the circle. What changes to cause this acceleration? (1)

   A ◯ The speed of the stone

   B ◯ The velocity of the stone

   C ◯ The direction of motion of the stone

   D ◯ The force of the stone

3. Give **two** examples of objects (other than the stone in questions 1 and 2) that travel in circular, or nearly circular, paths. (2)

   (a) ....

   (b) ....

4. Cyclotrons are particle accelerators. Use the following words to complete the passage below. (3)

   circular   **particles**   **speed**   **charged**   **magnetic field**

   Cyclotrons produce a force on .... particles. This force is provided by a

   .... which makes the particles move in a .... or spiral path.

   The .... of the .... increases as they travel along the path.

5. What is the difference between an **elastic** collision and an **inelastic** collision? (4)

   ....

   ....

   ....

   ....

   ....

   ....

6. Two bodies collide at various speeds. Complete the table below about the total momentum and kinetic energy before and after the collision. (3)

Momentum Before (kg m/s)	Momentum After (kg m/s)	KE Before (J)	KE After (J)	Elastic or Inelastic?
75	75	112.5	56.25	**(a)**
25	**(b)**	162.5	**(c)**	Elastic
(d)	50	50	25	**(e)**

7. This question is about PET scanners.

(a) What radiation is produced by the radioactive isotopes? Explain the process known as **annihilation**. (4)

....

....

....

(b) This process is an elastic collision. What **two** quantities are conserved?

(i) .... (1)

(ii) .... (1)

(c) Where does the energy of the emitted radiation come from? (3)

....

....

*8. Describe how cyclotrons can be used to produce the radioactive isotopes that are used in medical diagnosis. (6)

....

....

....

....

....

....

....

9. In electron-positron annihilation, an electron collides with a positron.

Explain how the following quantities are conserved.

(a) Charge (3)

....

....

(b) Momentum (3)

....

....

....

....

....

(Total: .... / 35)

---

10. A lorry of mass 2250kg travelling at 32m/s collides with a car of mass 750kg travelling in the same direction at a speed of 22m/s. After the collision, the two vehicles continue to move in the same direction together. Calculate the speed of the two vehicles. (4)

....

....

....

....

11. In a physics experiment, a billiard ball of mass 0.17kg is fired at a speed of 0.3m/s at another ball of mass 0.15kg, which is stationary. After collision, the first ball slows down to 0.029m/s, while the second one moves off in the same direction.

(a) Calculate the speed of the second ball after collision. (3)

....

....

....

continued...

(b) Show whether this collision is elastic or inelastic. (4)

12. Two spheres of equal mass are suspended from adjacent points.

One sphere is pulled back a little way and released so that it strikes the second sphere at 12cm/s. The collision is elastic. Describe and explain what happens to the motion of each sphere. (4)

(Total: .... / 15)

Questions labelled with an asterisk (*) are ones where the quality of your written communication will be assessed – you should take particular care with your spelling, punctuation and grammar, as well as the clarity of expression, on these questions.

1. Use the following words to label the diagrams below. (3)

liquid   solid   gas

(a) ....   (b) ....   (c) ....

2. What happens when the temperature of a gas increases?

A ◯ Gas molecules move more slowly than previously.

B ◯ A liquid is formed.

C ◯ There are fewer collisions between molecules than previously.

D ◯ The molecules of the gas move faster than previously.

3. A girl blows up a balloon for a party. Use the following words to complete the passage below about the air pressure inside the balloon. (3)

pressure   atmosphere   collide   greater   moving   force

Gas molecules are always .... They .... with the walls of

the balloon. This causes a .... on the walls which creates a

.... This is .... than the pressure of the

.... outside the balloon.

4. **(a)** What is absolute zero in degrees Celsius? .... (1)

(b) What does absolute zero mean in terms of the movement of molecules? (1)

....

5. **(a)** What is 0°C in kelvin?.. (1)

(b) What is 373K in degrees Celsius? .... (2)

6. The temperature of a gas is 100K. When the temperature is increased to 200K, what happens to:

(a) the speed of the molecules? .... (1)

(b) the kinetic energy of the molecules? .... (1)

7. The volume of a balloon **decreases** from an initial value of 800cm³ when the pressure of the air inside **increases** from 12 000Pa to 16 000Pa. The air in the balloon remains at constant temperature. Calculate the new volume of the balloon using the formula on page 100 to help you. (2)

*8. Briefly describe an experiment to investigate how the volume and pressure of a gas are related. Include a labelled diagram in your answer, if this helps. (6)

9. Ethan carries out an experiment to find out how the volume of air changes with temperature. He takes a plastic syringe and warms the air inside it by putting it in a beaker of water. The water is heated by a Bunsen. He measures the temperature and the volume of the air. His results are shown below.

Volume (cm³)	62	75	88
Temperature (°C)	0	50	100

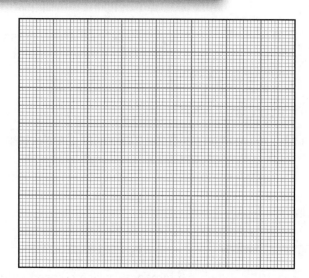

(a) Plot a graph of volume on the vertical-axis against the temperature on the horizontal-axis. (The temperature axis should extend from −300°C to 100°C.) Draw the best fit straight line and extend it back so that it reaches the temperature axis. (2)

(b) (i) From your graph, what is the temperature where the line meets the temperature-axis? (1)

(ii) What is this temperature called? (1)

(iii) What should it be? (1)

(c) Why are your answers to **(b)(i)** and **(b)(iii)** different? (2)

10. How would you investigate the relation between the temperature and the volume of a gas as accurately as possible?

(a) Describe an experiment that can be performed in a school laboratory. (3)

(b) Describe the results that you would expect. (2)

11. Nitrous oxide is a gas often used in medicine. Give **two** situations in which it is used.

(a) (1)

(b) (1)

12. A cylinder of oxygen gas is brought to the bedside of a patient with chronic lung disease.

(a) The gas is stored in the cylinder above atmospheric pressure. Why? (2)

(b) What is the purpose of the pressure regulating valve? (2)

....

....

....

(Total: .... **/ 39)**

Higher Tier

13. Butane gas is kept in a small cylindrical container under a pressure of 80kPa at 22°C. The seal may leak if the pressure exceeds 90kPa. At what temperature in °C will the container begin to leak butane gas? (4)

....

....

14. A gas cylinder has an internal volume of 12 litres. If the volume of the gas compressed in the cylinder is 600 litres, calculate the pressure of the gas above atmospheric pressure. (2)

....

....

15. A large oxygen cylinder contains 3500 litres of compressed oxygen. Its pressure gauge reads 211kPa. Assuming the temperature is held constant:

(a) what volume of oxygen can be released at atmospheric pressure (101kPa)? (2)

....

....

(b) If the flow rate is adjusted to 5 litres per minute, how many days would it take to empty the cylinder? (2)

....

....

(Total: .... **/ 10)**

Formulae Sheet

P1

Wave speed (metre/second, m/s) = frequency (hertz, Hz) × wavelength (metre, m) $\quad v = f \times \lambda$

Wave speed (metre/second, m/s) = $\dfrac{\text{distance (metre, m)}}{\text{time (second, s)}}$ $\quad v = \dfrac{x}{t}$

Electrical power (watt, W) = current (ampere, A) × potential difference (volt, V) $\quad P = I \times V$

Calculating the cost of the electricity:
cost (p) = power (kilowatts, kW) × time (hour, h) × cost of 1 kilowatt-hour (p/kW h)

Power (watt, W) = $\dfrac{\text{energy used (joule, J)}}{\text{time taken (second, s)}}$ $\quad P = \dfrac{E}{t}$

Efficiency = $\dfrac{\text{useful energy transferred by the device}}{\text{total energy supplied to the device}} \times 100\%$

P2

Charge (coulomb, C) = current (ampere, A) × time (second, s) $\quad Q = I \times t$

Potential difference (volt, V) = current (ampere, A) × resistance (ohm, Ω) $\quad V = I \times R$

Electrical power (watt, W) = current (ampere, A) × potential difference (volt, V) $\quad P = I \times V$

Energy transferred (joule, J) = current (ampere, A) × potential difference (volt, V) × time (second, s) $\quad E = I \times V \times t$

Speed (metre per second, m/s) = $\dfrac{\text{distance (metre, m)}}{\text{time (second, s)}}$

Acceleration (metre per second squared, m/s^2) = $\dfrac{\text{change in velocity (metre per second, m/s)}}{\text{time taken (second, s)}}$ $\quad a = \dfrac{(v - u)}{t}$

Force (newton, N) = mass (kilogram, kg) × acceleration (metre per second squared, m/s^2) $\quad F = m \times a$

Weight (newton, N) = mass (kilogram, kg) × gravitational field strength (newton per kilogram, N/kg) $\quad W = m \times g$

momentum (kilogram metre per second, kg m/s) = mass (kilogram, kg) × velocity (metre per second, m/s) $\quad momentum = m \times v$

Work done (joule, J) = force (newton, N) × distance moved in the direction of the force (metre, m) $\quad E = F \times d$

Power (watt, W) = $\dfrac{\text{work done (joule, J)}}{\text{time taken (second, s)}}$ $\quad P = \dfrac{E}{t}$

Gravitational potential energy (joule, J) = mass (kilogram, kg) × gravitational field strength (newton per kilogram, N/kg) × vertical height (metre, m)
$GPE = m \times g \times h$

Kinetic energy (joule, J) = $\dfrac{1}{2}$ × mass (kilogram, kg) × velocity^2 ([metre/second]^2 [m/s]^2) $\quad KE = \dfrac{1}{2} \times m \times v^2$

Formulae Sheet

Force (newton, N) = $\dfrac{\text{change in momentum (kilogram metre per second, kg m/s)}}{\text{time (second, s)}}$

$$F = \frac{(mv - mu)}{t}$$

P3

Power of lens (dioptre, D) = $\dfrac{1}{\text{focal length (metre, m)}}$

Frequency (hertz, Hz) = $\dfrac{1}{\text{time period (second, s)}}$ $\qquad f = \dfrac{1}{T}$

The relationship between temperature and volume for a gas (at constant temperature): $\qquad V_1 = \dfrac{V_2\, T_1}{T_2}$

(where V_1 and T_1 represent the initial volume and temperature and V_2 and T_2 represent the final volume and temperature (temperature in K))

The relationship between volume and pressure for a gas (at constant temperature): $\qquad V_1 P_1 = V_2 P_2$

(where V_1 and P_1 represent the initial volume and pressure and V_2 and P_2 represent the final volume and pressure (pressure in Pa))

Intensity (watt per metre squared, W/m²) = $\dfrac{\text{power of incident radiation (watt, W)}}{\text{area (metre squared, m}^2\text{)}}$ $\qquad I = \dfrac{P}{A}$

The focal length of a lens f is related to the object distance, u and the image distance, v by the following equation:
(f = focal length [m], u = object distance [m], v = image distance [m]) $\qquad \dfrac{1}{f} = \dfrac{1}{u} + \dfrac{1}{v}$

Current (ampere, A) = number of particles per second (1/second, 1/s) × charge of one particle (coulomb, C) $\qquad I = N \times q$

Kinetic energy (joule, J) = electronic charge (coulomb, C) × accelerating potential difference (volt, V) $\qquad KE = \dfrac{1}{2} mv^2 = e \times V$

The relationship between the volume, pressure and temperature for a gas:

$\dfrac{\text{initial pressure (pascal, Pa)} \times \text{initial volume (metre}^3\text{, m}^3\text{)}}{\text{initial temperature (kelvin, K)}} = \dfrac{\text{final pressure (pascal, Pa)} \times \text{final volume (metre}^3\text{, m}^3\text{)}}{\text{final temperature (kelvin, K)}}$

$$\frac{P_1 V_1}{T_1} = \frac{P_2 V_2}{T_2}$$